THE PILGRIM

A TIMELESS JOURNEY TO THE CRYSTAL CITY OF MACHU PICCHU

THE PILGRIM

A TIMELESS JOURNEY TO THE
CRYSTAL CITY OF MACHU PICCHU

MALLKU

Evelyn Guimarães de Paiva
Alanna Aisha Aribalo

Original Title:
Peregrina Universal
Viaje Intemporal a la Ciudad Cristal de Machu Picchu
English Translation: ALBERTO MIORI SANZ
English Correction: HELENITA ZIEGLER

Author Editor:
Evelyn Guimarães de Paiva – Alanna Aisha
1ra Edición

The Pilgrim
A Timeless Journey to the
Crystal City of Machu Picchu

Composition, photographic art, drawings, diagrams: Mallku
Digital art: Carlos Paullo Rodríguez
Paintings: Gonzalo Medina

Hecho el Depósito Legal en la Biblioteca Nacional del Perú N° 2008-04186
ISBN: 987-9972-33-731-4

Cusco – Peru, 2008

To my Parents Ludmar and Dilcy,
for existing and allowing me to be born.

I wish to dedicate this book to all the Beings of Light who guide me,
to my protectors who work in the light,
to Pachamama –Mother Earth–
and the Great Spirit of Wiraqocha.

To all who participated directly
or indirectly in my life.

To the Spiritual Leaders
whom I met in this physical plane and in the subtle ones.

Together we form one family.
Together we form one heart that radiates love.
Together we are many and we are one.

Offering with "qoqa kintu"
and the Sacred Fire (Willka Nina).

CONTENTS

Meditation in the Andes.

INTRODUCTION

It is my wish to share this novel with you where I tell about the merger of four Shazadi's lives. This name means Princess in Arabian language. She was created to show more about the experiences in life, the transformations and rebirths of a person who is aware of life passages. In this book I recount her trials and tribulations and how she was delivered from them as well as the apprenticeships she served freeing her from energetic ties, achieving clearer vision, thoughts and feelings throughout her entire process of change.

I wish to share the result of a centuries-long research of Shazadi's life. The greatest of these findings was the acknowledgement of her inner strength and capacity to transform any reality, since that which is real is our own inner world with the external merely a reflection. We learn much more through the experiences and teachings of others and, if we are genuine, we share our own as well.

I am happy to write this book and express what I have come to learn over time that I am not perfect, but travel down an endless path of self growth and expansion. When open and accessible to life, we no longer falter but are transformed as we learn we are just part of a continuous energetic flow.

Once we embark on the path of "BEING," we assume another view of the world, since we understand that it is we who construct it. If someone carries out his/her part and fulfills their energized mission, they are contributing to the creation of a better world. I learned, that we can't change anyone, only modify what is inside of us.

It is important first, to know our emotions and feelings, our body and the limitations of the moment from the conflicts that occur, to be overcome as we progress. Then we see that change is ever-present in our lives, modifying our environment to show us the reality of our inner power. We must be conscious of this power to show us the richness of the physical and the spiritual worlds.

We must learn that life goes beyond the simple, beyond the basic, even beyond material wealth and is dependent on our vision of the world to be able to accept a life with freedom. The freedom of consciousness allows us to create an authentic life with one of higher values.

Humankind needs to recognize its own inner strength. We all possess knowledge and experiences, which we bring from previous lives and, since it is all interconnected, there is no separation with the Universe. To think that our family is one and only and unique is an illusion of a small world filled with restrictions. Our family is much greater, it is created by all who participate in the internal expansion within the Light.

The discovery of inner forces is necessary and becomes challenging, for it sometimes is often easier to conform with the exterior and superficial manifestations of a simple life with the routine path becoming even more convenient, with less toil and minimum challenge. Personal confrontation of oneself and one's fears is the gateway that allows us to discover who we really are and enabling us to grow responsibly. To learn and acknowledge truth, in the sense of personal authenticity, is an arduous task, yet one that in the end yields great satisfaction. To be authentic is a daring challenge, it is the path to freedom, which leads us to become queens and kings, gods and goddesses, of our own lives for in essence that is what we truly are. Time and Space are merely states of our own divinity.

Our emotions and experiences are stored and recorded in our DNA and as we are released from our energetic fetters from the past, we can fully assume and engage in our present reality.

More people are realizing and acknowledging the importance of well being, of being satisfied in the preservation of the divine in humanity with the numbers opening themselves to this path constantly increasing. In my inner journeys I discovered the mountains of the Andes and how this land of Pachamama radiates its mantle of light over the entire Planet. Life led me to know these mountains of power and to walk upon their sacred ground. In the Andes, I learned to ground my power and consciously activate my *chakras*, the energy centers located along my spinal chord.

It is necessary to be open to life in order to acquire the capacity to modify our paths, leaving behind what we are no longer need to carry. This is that way we witness fantastic results and recognize our soul, which guides us to open our heart and, when inhaling, we realize that not only our lungs are functioning but rather our total self, manifesting the act of unconditional love that enables us to live in purity and authenticity.

As unique beings, we are aware of the need for people to awaken, to remove themselves from basic existence, which is just a poor reflection in respect to their own spiritual path. For the world surrounds them in a halo of illusion and turns them into slaves of their own desires and fantasies, wasting away their own existence locking them into debt and obligations because of their ignorance. This in turn only serves to fill them with dissatisfaction at the stark shallowness of the life they've accepted in exchange. This leads them to crave more and more material goods, which then create further complications through the realization of yet more dissatisfactions and failures.

When an individual strays away from, or abandons his path of inner peace, that person finds sickness and malaise, even suicide and becomes dependant on tranquilizers and therapies for relief from the numerous imbalances that assail him. Stress is a temporary malaise that affects the natural principles of growth and maturity of a person. Hence, with the passing of years, as we age, we once again become like children. And if our life was full of shallowness and insignificance, this elderly-child will be an unsatisfied person, feel abandoned and neglected, and begin to lose the sense of joy in life. Because not knowing what more life can offer, that individual has to undergo moments of great inner difficulty and insecurity. Obviously, life can be different than that. It depends on whether we decide here and now to make a change toward a higher phase of development to create spiritual and material balance.

I also wish to share matters and issues concerning the energy of love with you. The most powerful of energies extant within the realm of human existence is that of creation, the energy of the power of transformation. That is sexual energy, the energy of *Kundalini*, expressed symbolically in the form of an alchemical serpent. Love is, in its absolute totality, one great energetic expression that teaches us to grow spiritually. With this energy, the creativeness of the individual is enhanced and he or she becomes more acutely aware in dealing with the subtleties and insights of the world at large.

The passage of time and the school of life were my great allies in self-discovery, by virtue of being a woman, coexisting physically and emotionally with other beings, I was able to learn about my own strengths and weaknesses. Along a similar line of thought, as a woman I wish to not only vindicate but also clearly assert the principle of sexual freedom and the full conscientiousness of it within those of feminine sex —in other words, without any tinge of guilt and far from the creed of sin.

Throughout history we witness the continuous repression of women, even at the level of their own personal pleasure. In present times we are confronted with examples in the Middle East, in Africa and in more than a few indigenous cultures of the "New World" (such as the Amazonian Region of Peru), where women, upon reaching a certain age, undergo removal of their clitoris. This is done generally by claiming religious reasons, in what constitutes a flagrant act of aggression, contempt and abuse of their personal freedom. The concept of "being a woman" is very broad and the sensations of pleasure depend on how that "being a woman" is sustained in accordance with that individual's personal desires.

It is my hopeful wish that this book may awaken in you the strength and will to "Dare" in your lives, so that you may understand to "Be" and thus reduce your dependence to "Have," since over the course of time, so many acquisitions in our lives become so utterly unnecessary.

It is through the medium of poetry that I express events and happenings of the soul, which are in essence thoughts rooted and based in ancient experiences and emotions.

I neither propose nor subscribe to the idea that we should, at present, continue to dwell in trees and depend solely upon the fruits of nature for sustenance; nor that we should only wait expectantly upon the advent of miracles. There is more to life than that. This book, for example, is made possible by technology created by human beings. In discerning our true necessities, we should nonetheless prioritize just that which is appropriate and conducive to our spiritual path. In that way we scan attain freedom, slaves no longer of "Having" and devote our time to growth knowing that this is an unique opportunity.

Only then shall we arrive at the realization that we can identify our own strength without loss of tenderness, without being any less gentle. For inner strength must nevertheless always be closely associated with sweetness. By placing feeling and sensitivity in all our endeavors, will we find the beauty in ourselves. Only when we express ourselves through our art, will we be able to recognize life in its myriad manifestations, where beauty is endowed with many forms and expressions of its own. Moving about in the company of beauty teaches us our own charm. To no one or anything other than ourselves need we offer or feel compelled to show proof of this our personal treasure, for if we feel we must, then we become captives of someone else's judgment, and so lose the gift of feeling our own grace.

The weakness of many women lies in competing among one another to attain or secure their own space. A situation narrowed to that of striving to show she is better and prettier than the other, makes you forget that only when realizing one's inner beauty will it forever shine, even into old age. If one seeks an inner path, this beauty will be gifted with even greater light and harmony. In the Shamanic way lies the path of beauty and pleasure.

Humankind is blinded by the illusion that growth is achieved through suffering (forgetting that the root of growth is the pleasure) and proclaiming it is our duty to be free from emotional burdens and penitential tasks for the purposes of cleansing ourselves of pains, sufferings and guilt –in short, sins. Most religions show a fondness for teaching that divine order is to be reached through suffering. The principal result of this sort of ignorant belief has been, and continues to be so till this very day, that of creating countless hindrances and obstacles to impede the Soul from transcending the barriers that keep it detained.

The path of inner growth may seem more difficult, yet with discipline and time, this road becomes more sound and secure, as well as clearer to follow. In shamanism we do have confrontations while living our lives, yet the key to that lies in recognizing the ultimate reality is one that lies beyond our own limitations. It is at that moment when the transitory nature of realities, that which affects our equilibrium, can be transformed to last forever.

In the Shamanic path, we learn to die to be reborn, to rise once more triumphant, expressing power along with sweetness and sensitivity. Paradise is here and now and one must undertake a constructive and pleasurable life at all levels.

It is in the simplicity of the moment with an open heart that spiritual peace is found. By journeying deep into our self do we realize the greatness and the worthiness of our value.

The divine essence of every Self is the reflection of the beauty that exists within the Universe.

The Power's Centers are very specific sites and places that exist on our planet. In these Centers there is a flow of vital waves and currents, emanating energy, thus forming energetic nuclei. The people who dwell there develop an evolved level of inner growth, highly knowledgeable in the Esoteric Sciences of the Universe. Currently to live in these Centers is the privilege of few. Where people feel touched by the strength of the energy flow, their hearts open up and, along with Solar Initiations, expand their full potential, hence living better.

There are moments when Shazadi travels in time and space through visions and partakes of initiations that impulse her growth and development.

As Universal Pilgrim, I invite you to journey through your personal inner world!

The Authoress.

Cosmic Connections

PART ONE

The Great Teaching is that we can
have a life of love and
accomplishments; and the option of
good living is an art, depending on
whether we decide to Dare to change.

EGYPT

In the delta of the Nile all was green, with large trees and birds who inhabited their canopies. It was a small heaven on earth, a paradise that radiated peace.

Even to this day, Shazadi, who dwelled in those lands and in the time of the great pharaohs, remembered and could feel its fragrance, hear its sounds and visualize the colors of the people. She was in Egypt, and a great energetic surge rooted her to these lands. She could see herself walking among the royal gardens of the resort palace, on the shores of the great river which spawned into the Southern Lake. This lake marked the middle of the world or equatorial line, which bestowed a divine and magical origin upon it, indicating the polarity of the world. It was here in these places where she would recall the story of her beloved.

The lands were fertile, thus allowing for the development of one of the most outstanding cultures of humankind, a society of great technological accomplishments as well as cosmological and stellar knowledge. This is where, under unknown circumstances, Shazadi met a plebeian who awakened her to the emotion of love. Due to the insurmountable social differences of caste and origin between them, they found themselves obligated to devise ways to love each other in secret. These are her memories:

Shazadi did not feel free, because she was living in an enormous palace that included many nobles, guardians and servants. At times she felt hemmed in and closely scrutinized. They addressed her as Princess Shazadi and she was bound to observe a certain amount of palace rules and protocol. But by far the most difficult and complex of these matters was the fact that her parents had betrothed her to Bernet, a prince of royal blood and member of the court. She was to marry him a year after the date of the official engagement. For a long time, the parents of both had keenly sought to unite them in order to preserve the royal line. But she didn't love him, and so, how could she be made to marry him? Only for the sake of formality and family hierarchy? This, for her, was absolutely unjust and disregarded her personal feelings; she felt the urge to escape, to disappear from this setting of illusion and fantasies.

She was as yet unaware of her inner strength and of the destinies that the Universe had in store for her. She was immature yet full of desire to grow, and wept at her own powerlessness to be able to solve her conflicts and insecurities. She felt very alone, and the only ray of hope she had was to go out to the gardens, on the banks of the great sacred river, to meet with Amrep, her forbidden love.

She knew that she would have to devise strategies to become free of her lineage and class, because her heart belonged to another man, the only one who had ever touched and awakened love in her. To come together with him was her cure, to allow the pains of her heart and body to vanish. When they loved each other, their lips formed one single being and their mutual caresses were like an ultimate expression of total oneness.

One day, as she gazed out her window at the clouds and the sky, Shazadi suddenly realized that she could understand the beauty of things, that her soul was capable of expressing this, and she wrote:

"We remain alive where our heart lies."

The wind touched her long black hair and rippled her beautiful dress of silky white. She walked barefoot, for it made her feel free and her sensations were enhanced by the direct contact with the earth, which in turn made her more aware and receptive to the subtleties of scents and tastes. She could give herself into nature with ease and explore her cellular motions through all their changes and metamorphoses. She could dance, feeling her soul asking for more, wanting to live every moment intensely. All of this filled her and at times thus inspired would express herself through verse, which allowed her to confront the opposites that lay in her own path: pain and love. Shazadi found in poetry a beautiful way of sharing with herself and others the discernment of insightful messages and teachings of life; the same that would gradually liberate her and make her a chosen one in search of happiness and self-assurance:

When I hear you, your scent I breathe.
When I breathe your scent, I feel you.
When you I feel, I love you.

When you I love, I desire you.
And resisting not,
I seek you.

When we acknowledge love, it becomes part of us, and life's expressions are filled with sense. It's necessary to experience love and to share with whom we love.

She could distinguish her inner visions, which at times intermixed and expressed themselves as remote scenes filled with pain that yearned to be healed. From within her then flowed words that said:

In the depth of your eyes
I sense that energy which moves me.
You warm me with your gaze
and within me I feel waves of love.
I am overcome by the need of touching you
and feeling your every part.

To feel loved is one of the delights of life, the nourishment of our cells. It leads to discovering our own mysteries, where even life itself becomes more alive... the complexion glowing, the eyes radiating happiness... like water's eyes.

EYES OF WATER

Eyes like those that gaze,
eyes like those that moisten.
Water that falls on each part of the Earth,
sensitivity of Eyes.
Sensitive eyes are always eyes of water
which possess depth and transparency, and
the Self as a whole, appears as eyes of water.
Those that are the transparencies of the Soul
and relate emotions.

Shazadi felt inspired, she knew that verses could narrate her own story, and she would make poetry transform into living flesh.

WHO I AM

In the intimacy of the seeking,
something will come to be known.
From love is made to grow
the joy of living.

Each day a hope is born
of finding a better world.
Setbacks and victories are part
of something born with wisdom.

Sadness calls at the door,
a storm departs.
In the awakening of a hope
is reborn the sparkle in an eye.

Happiness fills the breast
in the dawn of a morning clear.
Nature completes the Self
who with purpose walks.

In the paths it follows,
a light is suddenly kindled.
A new happening eventful
without regret or penance.

Shazadi often spent much of her time in the resort palace, and from her chambers delighted in the view of a sublime landscape, with gardens filled with myriad flowers that provided great inspiration, leading her to write, replicating her world with her absent lover. She furnished her living quarters with people and everything required to enlist nature as her ally: exotic animals, cameloids, dogs, and trees for birds to nest in. She saw in this inner chamber a home filled with love, peace and light, an ideal setting to share with her beloved one.

FRIENDSHIP

*In a life with ups and downs
a hope is born,
and with it the desire to live.
Situations to confront,
with a look we read thoughts
and different worlds to know.
A feeling grows stronger
with every day's experience.
Sincerity is nourishment,
support received.
Silent tears may be shed,
as an occurrence of acknowledgement.
With the passing of the mornings,
my home renews its energy
with the sharing of a beautiful friendship.*

Merkaya, a woman who worked in the palace, became Shazadi's servant, as well as part accomplice and part enemy of some of her whims and caprices, in particular of her silent escapes and ventures. One morning Shazadi awoke with a still quite vivid dream lingering. In it, she had spent the night with her paramour. She felt so happy that even Merkaya seemed to enjoy it all and, a smile playing on her lips, asked:

"Good Morning, my lady, did you sleep well? It seems as though you've seen pretty colored birdies!"

"Merkaya, I slept with my lover!," responded the Princess in a radiant tone, as she carried out her sacred dance practices and other exercises that formed part of the disciplines of the royal families.

"And who would that be?" asked Merkaya, "Someone who exists only in your dreams?"

"Ah! Do you not know that I have my lover and I always meet with him? But, this must be our secret. And I will need your help at certain times. You will help me, won't you?" Shazadi asked her.

"Yes, of course, I am here to serve you, my Lady," responded the servile yet traitorous Merkaya, who in her innermost felt envy and hatred against the Princess and perceived an opportunity to betray her.

"I am betrothed to a nobleman of the court," Shazadi innocently told her, "Prince Bernet. My parents and his agreed to marry us and thus sentenced me to an unknown love, one which is not mine. My heart belongs to another man and I believe I should escape and live with my true love. Merkaya, I need you to help me elope."

"Worry not, Princess, I am acquainted with some of the guards and will distract them at the precise moment so that you can get away without being noticed. If it's necessary, I shall procure a rope so that you can climb down from this window, and at you bidding, I shall deliver a letter to your parents explaining everything."

The Princess became extremely heartened at this, as well as happy for she was to later meet with her lover. She then decided to don a beautiful attire and perfume herself with exotic scents.

Yet, on that same morning, Merkaya went off to Prince Bernet and warned him of the Princess' forthcoming elopement as well as of her secret love with a plebeian. The prince was altogether surprised at the news. He rewarded the informer and secretly began to prepare a terrible vengeance.

Meanwhile, completely unaware of the trap being set, the Princess continued in a state of ecstatic reverie: she saw herself traveling through new lands in the company of the person who had shown her the path of love. And she turned her dreams into verse:

LONGING FOR YOU

With the song of birds,
ever-present symphony,
I feel life.
I am a happy person.

In the blue of sky,
the clouds mingle.
Beautiful formations
of a sparkling morning.

The wind tussles my hair,
brings with it deep remembrances.
And memory searches me
for a few seconds.

Doubts make their appearance
in a struggle of impulses.
I have you in my thought
and love in my heart.

The Sun burns my body,
but I feel not this scorching heat.
I want you with me.
I search, where are you?

Then suddenly, the servant woman appeared. Feigning distraction, she inquired:

"I was looking for you, Princess. By the way, pray tell, at what time are you trysting with your lover?"

Shazadi, with the candidness of a soul in love, informed Merkaya of everything, telling her that in two hour's time she would be in the arms of her secret love. She did, however, muster the afterthought of interrogating her:

"And why all these questions?"

"Because all I want is to help you, mistress," was Merkaya's astute response. "Come now, please, you can later tell me how your encounter went."

"All right", said Shazadi, all too willfully setting her mind at ease in order to return to her emotional and nostalgic journey.

She relived in her thoughts how and where she met the plebeian who has broken her heart. Her memory took her back to the village where, once upon a time, when carrying out charitable activities, she entered a humble dwelling and was confronted with the reality that within this extremely small space there lived as many as eight persons. She could not conceive how it could be possible to live under such conditions, or why they had not forsaken hope long ago. Saddened, she made her mind up to always pass this way and bring food and clothing to these needy peasant folk. Then one day, as she was walking away from the village and about to enter the royal gardens by the river bank she was suddenly surprised by the presence of a particularly muscular and well-built peasant going about his chores. His rather strapping and handsome appearance, as well as the dedicated concentration he placed upon his actions, got her attention and she felt an attraction in some way. She walked toward him and greeted him with a "Good Morning."

He reacted nervously at the sound of the delicate voice that suddenly broke into his physical routine and, upon turning around he was confronted with evidence that the world of angels had descended to this earth in the form of a beautiful and graceful woman. At the same time, her earthly origin was clearly evident by her attire, which revealed a noble origin. Without taking his eyes off her, he responded:

> "Good morning to you. I am Amrep and I live in this village. This is where I work in order to assist some of the families of my community."

She was already feeling somewhat ecstatic at perceiving in this peasant man the strength and conviction of someone who, with security and confidence, accepted his condition and took his work very seriously. Then she heard him ask:

> "And who are you?"

> "My name is Shazadi and I am passing through, visiting your village."

The connection had been established, the link had spawned the heart of the Princess and she felt vibrant at the encounter.

Amrep, in turn, remained somewhere betwixt between amazement and bewilderment at the presence of such a beautiful visitor. Unfortunately, however, she was forced to return to the palace, and it required more than a little for her to come back to her senses and take her leave. Amrep, motionless, followed her with his eyes, not missing the least detail of the sublime moment. Only the pounding of his heart reminded him that he was really there and that what he was witnessing was no fantasy, a product of his own simplicity.

Shazadi and Amrep were struck, overwhelmed and irremediably conquered by love. The two of them, strangers to one another, a few moments after meeting, became lovers. Their passion had so far remained secret for five months.

LOVE

*If the fulfillment of everything is Love,
the great fruit it yields is called Friendship.
When two people meet,
there is always a seed to plant.
And that seed is mutual support and commitment
to enable the sharing of our needs,
and thus reach the attainment of our longings.
The feeling that unites inward and outwardly,
becomes a part of ourselves.
As two vessels in an ocean lost,
both helping each other,
to find their way back home.
If we succeed in making the seed sprout,
at the end of all, we shall have reached
all that is our fulfillment: Love.*

On that day when Shazadi began to seriously consider escape and flight, she went off in search of her lover to inform him of her decision. As usual, she was shrouded in a long black veil to avoid being recognized. But when somewhere close to the halfway point, where the gardens began, she felt the presence of someone following her. It was a brief impression, so that a short time later she actually found herself considering that it may have been only her imagination. Nevertheless, upon reaching the point of rendezvous with Amrep, she told him of her misgivings, warning him to remain very alert.

Then Shazadi broke the news that she was determined to elope with him, because she could not withstand the thought of marrying a courtier whom she was not in love with.

> "I love you very much and dream of having a family with you, and I want us to build a home where I can be fulfilled, in your company," was her loving and sincere confession as they kissed passionately.

Amrep, however, who seemed struck by surprise at the turn of events, merely responded:

> "You must be very sure of what you're doing. As the simple peasant that I am, I don't have very much to offer you compared to the lifestyle you are accustomed to leading in palace. And I feel that love would have a difficult time surviving amongst privations."

But Shazadi had made her decision, she did mind living in modest conditions away from courtly privileges. She believed herself to be ready to love, and the blindness of her love did not gauge consequences. What did anything matter, if at the end of it all her love would awaken her and lead her to acknowledging her virtues and inner wisdom? What did trouble her was the sense of doubt she perceived in her lover and was surprised by his failure to see that a relationship is created through a common existence, a mutual participation, for nothing set into a pattern of permanence –only the act of learning is eternal. She had a premonitory feeling that perhaps Amrep was not on the same frequency.

Shazadi's words were not sufficient to fully convince Amrep, and the ensuing disillusion led her mind astray causing her to forget altogether the feeling she had had about someone following her. But, sure enough, behind a tree stood Bernet, observing their every movement expecting that his royal wrath would overcome him at any moment. But he found himself feeling quite self-contained, preferring a more elaborate vengeance. He turned and left, returning to the palace to plan.

Shazadi felt that Amrep's response had hurt her deeply, but she was in love and did not want to awaken from this beautiful dream, deciding that it was worth running the risk. Amrep insinuated that it was wiser to live the moment, and both surrendered to their passions, with only the trees as silent witnesses of their physical alchemy. Time and space vanished for them, until the cool breeze of nightfall brought them back to reality and Shazadi realized it was time to return to the palace.

Back in her chambers, she came upon Merkaya and indicated that she was not in the mood to speak with her, giving orders to not be disturbed for she felt indisposed. In her bedroom she meditated long over Amrep's words and the thought crossed her mind that perhaps he didn't love her, or not as much as she loved him, to the point where he was not willing to fight for his love nor even face the difficulties which could arise. Yet she was prepared to share the simplicity and hardship of life and to fight to improve it. Meanwhile, the night became an endless ordeal and she poured out her thoughts and reflections in a poem:

BEAUTIFUL NIGHT

Night. Beautiful night!
The Moon lights the Sky,
in her grace filled shadow
reminding a new morning will come.

Music beckons to me,
the thoughts fly
to encounter doubts
which suddenly die.

In a life full of conflicts
a new decision,
unexpected situations,
I feel my heart beating.

The wind blows
in perfect harmony.
In the background silence,
questions loom.

The ants continue their labor
of seeking sustenance,
the breeze touches upon the desert
bringing sweet messages.

After many hours, Shazadi was able to sleep, although awakened many times, tears still streaming down her face. A persistent nightmare tormented her, the same one that came back night after night. Her sighing and moaning woke the servant woman, who came to see her, though her concern went no further than to learn more of the Princess' doings.

The new day came, heralded by the songs of birds. Both brought a sense of relief to Shazadi, who then wrote:

Dreams into dreams.

THE ART OF LIVING

The art of living is in each moment
and through life forever.
It is a marvel to be present in body and soul
and to add up so many experiences.
It is placing all effort and feeling
within each moment of time,
in each part of the earth.
Being what one is, without measure to love,
to possess the joy of living from the heart.
Silence speaks unceasingly,
and words conceal thoughts.
The Feminine, deep within,
brings with it inspiration, and the importance
of loving and being loved.
To talk much, or to speak little?
Listen more or hear less?
Words that teach us,
that we know only part of what we are,
and of what we can be.

EMOTIONS

Everything happens so suddenly…
And within the range of possibilities,
I assimilate the sensations.
In passive moments
when emotions rule.

Positive energy startles my body.
Tranquil mind of a love sincere.
Living that love intensely
floating in air suspended,
with life sprouting in each cell,
in each look,
in every depth.

A stimulus is born.
Recreating the will.
Perceiving myself,
in search of myself.

I know my instincts.
Humanity unique.
Reflecting Universal Love,
The one and only, great, LOVE.

Feelings of closeness.
I listen to the wind.
Pure energy,
who wants to give a bit of itself.

Poetry and ritual sacred dance were the forms in which Shazadi expressed herself. She placed her thoughts and emotions in her movements and her verses. In this way, she freed herself and paid tribute to the beauty of

LIFE

In the intimacy of happiness
we found a way.
The blue of sky becomes more vivid,
a way through which we reach fulfillment.
Nature interconnects us
in the sweetness of her contrasts.
We embark upon the quest
of a destination lost.
A stimulus is born,
a look of hunger.
In an instant of reflection
we sense the help that comes to us, mature.

Dreams were sources of inspiration for Shazadi, live messages that revealed to her the future, the outcome of many things. She had realized that life with her lover would be short and asked herself why. Did love from at least one partner, not suffice? Why should things not happen as she expected them to? She then decided to let it all flow, like waters of a river.

At the other end, the Shazadi's woes mattered in the least to her servant, who continued in the pursuit of her plot in cahoots with Bernet. Early one morning she encountered the Prince and he inquired:

"Have you anything new to tell me about the Princess?"

"Last night she was extremely upset and wished to speak to no one," Merkaya told him. "She constantly sighed and moaned in her sleep."

What they didn't know was that in Shazadi's nightmare, the Princess had seen how the soldiers of the court murdered her lover.

Meanwhile, Bernet had already planned the execution of his vengeance, which would be accomplished very discreetly, leaving no traces, availing himself of a courtly festival and the arrival of the Queen that was to take place in a few days' time.

In the afternoon, the Princess set out to meet Amrep. For her, these were moments eagerly awaited; for him, part of a strange routine that his simplicity knew not how to explain and so far accepting them simply as they presented themselves.

He often lay resting under the shade of a tree, close by the bank of the Nile, as if concealing himself from the challenge of destiny. He'd told the Princess that he could not yet live with her and that, as they had so far presented themselves, things were all right. Shazadi understood that, for him, survival weighed more than the love he professed for her. Notwithstanding that, their encounters retained for her their intensity of feeling and she was fascinated at experiencing the risks and dangers entailed. On his part, expert in the ways of nature and knowledgeable of every plant and creature, he remained a peasant and this trait clouded his comprehension to realize what Shazadi offered.

After each tryst, the Princess hurriedly returned, in order to not give rise to any suspicions and although things were not developing as she wished, she considered them satisfactory and expressed herself in verse:

HOPE

When night falls
a new light will shine in the sky.
Pointing out to me
the way which I should go.

In every road
there are always windows and doors open
and a feeling, a perception, pointing out
the window or door to enter by.

Difficult as any road may be,
there is always a way in and out.
Desire brings movement
and the light at the tunnel's end: Hope.
She always lies awaiting.
Do you prefer to wait?

In one of their latest encounters, Amrep had told her:

"I am doing my best to make your dreams come true, but in order for this to happen it is necessary that we leave this city. Even so, I have my doubts if it will work out, for I do not believe that this relationship can last over time. Everything becomes routine."

Shazadi was devastated, because she never expected this from him. Nevertheless, her obstinate mind continued to think about an urgent flight to uncertain destinations with her always at his side to help him succeed. And if escape were the way, it would have to happen soon.

All that day she reflected and finally understood that life has it's own ideals, which motivate every individual. They are the ideals, the dreams which all of us must have. This inspired her and she composed:

IDEALS

The dawning of the Sun heralds the coming of a new day. Enough time to accomplish what one desires. The search of an ideal consists within the struggle to reach goals and the hope of satisfying them. The sparkle of glance reveals desires and unforgettable situations in which we sometimes find ourselves. In the unchanging monotony of the day, life becomes a prisoner and many times smothers the desire and quest of something better. The day-to-day life forces us to repeat events, as if we were programmed to be unhappy and always complain. Many times, we forget that we are persons, we forget to live and to dream. One lives amid intense processes of internal conflict. When stumbling, one sometimes views the goal sought after from another perspective. And that is where these reflections come to rest. At the end of the day we watch the setting of the Sun, which offers us a beautiful spectacle. The air is scented, the birds fly to their nests, and some doors shut while others open. The desert wind heralds the closeness of the night with the New Moon and shining stars everything is renewed. The ultimate darkness tells us we have reached the end, but also the beginning of a new world.

Shazadi was a beautiful and sensual woman. Her forms expressed the charm of nature, yet she still felt a prisoner of her own body. Freedom came to her when she explored her sexuality. She understood that the purity of her love and the sharing of it showed her the ways of exaltation.

One morning, casually encountering Bernet, she sensed the way he looked at her. Though she was aware that her fate in the palace was cast, for it was her parent's will. She knew then and there that breaking from it would bring about the most serious confrontation and conflict in her life, for she was not disposed to give herself to any man other than Amrep.

LOVE DIVINE

In the warmest gaze
lies always endless emotions,
to which we surrender our self.
Lips find each other
and form part of the music
where tongues perform motions
in accordance with the intensity
of the beats of the heart.
A wave of love brings on desire, limitless desire.
It makes us rise and reach the summit of a high mountain.
The body trembles.
They seek each other more and more.
Garments torn in the yearning of living love.
In every point a freshness of feeling.
The willingness to always be.
Many caresses, touching, scents
feeding the desire to give oneself.
Continuous movements are a part of this dance
in which the dancer seeks his partner
not allowing her to escape.
Another world is entered.
Past harmonies and melodies do not invade the moment.
Breathing reaches a highest level.
We sail upon the same sea,
in the same vessel and with the same intention.
Bodies in unison of hunger to begin anew.
The insatiable thirst that never ends.
Permanence within the wild passion that joins two beings.
Brief movements. Bodies tremble
craving with desire to feel yet more ecstasy.
Reach orgasm in delirium.
Press together frenzied
and kiss flooded in love.
They are back in the world of always,
which at some point will perish.
Fire love. Passion that beckons.
Unconscious want, to give myself completely.
Sensation of life.
Wishing you in a world where we are both in one.
Surrounded in love.
I and you, you and I.

These words brought to Shazadi's memories and visions of the significance of total love that allowed one to surrender herself to a beloved, enter into communion with him with full liberty, stripped naked to experience confidence and trust before the person loved as a celebration of life. She felt that the frailty of her nature did not cause her to lose any strength.

In spite of her status and condition as Princess, she was only too aware of the sad reality of the feminine element surrounding her. The towns women existed within a state of physical, material and spiritual repression and the women of the court, although possessing of more freedom, were not trained in the arts of love and abandonment. In the course of her living there, Shazadi had managed to develop an open discussion and instruction among the women willing to free themselves, regardless of their social status.

But in order to further pursue it, it was necessary for Shazadi herself to learn more about the various aspects available at that time. And these, although limited, would provide basic information regarding sexuality and feminine affairs —topics to be addressed with the utmost discretion before royalty. But Shazadi felt confident, for she counted on her mother's support, who was committed to educating women. Though not an easy task, through the years it was gradually yielding fruitful results for their people and women were slowly changing and improving their lives.

Nevertheless, the current situation of the Princess, did not allow for self-fulfillment, the result of the changes that the intimate contact with her lover had brought about in her. She knew that the time would come when she would be unable to stay away from him and she would have to hasten her escape plans. As a result, she then wrote a letter to her parents:

My Dear Mother and Father

I know that you will both understand, for I am at a moment of my life in which I cannot afford to waste the opportunities that it offers me. I have met a special man and have fallen in love with him. He is a peasant and very wise in the ways of nature. From the first moment I saw him, my heart beat stronger and truer and I knew that I would give myself to him. We have spent many moments together and have shared our different worlds. Being close to him fills me with joy.

I do not love Bernet and have no desire to marry him. I have been meeting with my lover for several months and we walk and sing and laugh together; I feel it is important to share this happiness with you. Nevertheless, I must choose and make a decision because I feel that something bad will happen to Amrep, the name of my lover. I know that he is being stalked and watched from the palace but I have not managed to discover by whom. Thus, I have decided to elope with him and stay away until everything settles. I shall soon be in contact with you to let you know where we are living. I do so much want to continue seeing you both.

I am expecting a child and want you to know your grandson. Everything will turn out well and in three days we shall be leaving, though as of yet I know not our destination. I beseech you to support me and to understand that I wish to make a family of my own and create something different than all that I have thus far known. This is my opportunity to do so.

I beg of you to speak with Bernet after my departure, in order that he does not follow or seek me out. I understand that he will not accept my being with another man.

I wish happiness and peace to you both. I love you.

Until we meet again, your daughter

Shazadi

I dedicate to both of you this poem expressing the gratefulness of a person to her Father and Mother:

FATHER

In a given moment
the strolling gait of happiness
grew larger in stride.
The will to live grew broader
and responsibility grew greater.
A motive for struggle
in a life of contradictions.
A hope is born as love expands.

MOTHER

Your sweet look reveals much.
Affection blooms.
The will to live grows.
Hearts beat,
a new child comes to the world,
yet another moment that flies,
its life divided with a new being.
Symbol of strife, synonym of Love.
Reason for living in the search for courage.
Tenderness in the gaze.
Sweetness in her hands.
River that runs and shelters,
saves and surges once more,
overcoming situations
with intuitions of life.
I hold you in my heart and soul.
I love you and your way of being.
I shall never forget
the day when I emerged from your womb
and you entered my heart
to never again leave.

The Princess felt gratitude for her parents. She had forgiven them for not respecting her liberty for she understood that marriage arrangements through parents were a custom of the times. She knew that some rules were imposed due to the way they lived, but she had also understood that each person has their own path and that her moment to decide had come. On the other hand, she had learned to recognize the best in each person she had known during her life and, seeking out the beauty that each one of them possessed, she improved her own way of living. She always knew how to avail herself of the riches hidden within silence and attained an awakening of conscience that transformed her into a mature woman.

Then Shazadi arranged her belongings, preferring to take long loose clothing that would prove more comfortable during her pregnancy.

As was customary in the palace, Shazadi's parents were often away and she had at her disposal ample times of silence that allowed her to find herself. For this reason she knew that her parents would take a long time to stop missing her and yearning for her presence.

The indecisions she felt at times were overcome by the sureness that she would soon be joining her lover, since her elopement was a decided fact. She prepared for the radical changes she would face in her new life in addition to her pregnancy. In her next meeting with Amrep, she would tell him of her happiness and joy at this.

There were three days left before her escape and she decided to see her lover and tell him of the planned date as well as the happy news of the child she now carried in her womb. Upon meeting with Amrep she was pleasantly surprised for he brought gifts for her including a spirited well-bred horse for the forthcoming journey, although the fragrant colorful flowers were what she liked most. The news of her pregnancy was well received by Amrep with joy and enthusiasm. Both joined in the moment and took a promising first step.

The Princess returned to the Palace, avoided Merkaya's pretended solicitude, preferring to go to her chamber to meditate. There, she had a vision:

THE SACRED MOUNTAINS

She dwelled in the mountains, land of wise sages, and had been trained in various arts, principally in the path of inner alchemy. She learned that the physical discipline of warrior woman did not have to mar her beauty and sensuality. As a woman of conquest and wisdom, she was accompanied by another warrior: "The Messenger from the Heights," and between the two they taught the people, utilizing their Shamanic life as their main standard.

These two people were Shazadi and a lover, who from time to time were reborn to create new beneficial ways among their peoples. He, however, was not Amrep but another man, who had accompanied Shazadi in different times and places.

The vision showed her life in a valley surrounded by great looming peaks. Then, she climbed the sacred mountain of the most powerful bird in the world and there made offerings in a ceremony with the Wind, the Sun, the Earth, the Water and other creatures of power—the Llama, the Serpent, the Hummingbird, the Kondor and the Puma. She communed with the Mother Earth and the Sky and asked for enlightenment on her road to the Realm of the Unnamed, who in these lands was known as "Pachakamaq." All of this was part of cleansing, purification and liberation to fly together with the Sacred Kondor.

Shazadi knew that this was one of the visions that enabled her to see herself in the context of her multiple lives, though this was a very special one, for it returned to her warrior life. Nature was brilliant and the messengers of the sky, such as the Rainbow, more vivid, a faithful portrait of the Akashic memory of these sacred people. All of this chorus and powerful energy made Shazadi intone a mantra to the Mother Earth, which expanded and vibrated as PACHAMAMA. Shazadi in this way showed her gratitude for everything she had received in this land filled with magic.

For in these mountains she learned through the sages, that placing her left hand on her solar plexus, and her right hand on her heart was an expression of gratitude and communion with the forces of the Earth and the Sky. The left hand, which must come from the direction of the Earth, brings with it the strength of the

Mother and the right hand descends with the strength of the Sky. When positioned upon the solar plexus and the heart respectively these connect the individual with Life itself and with the Universe. In this manner, Shazadi positioned her hands to thank the Earth and the Sky for all she had received in these cities of light. Then, bit by bit, she started reacquiring consciousness of herself, until returning to her own time and space.

That night Shazadi had entered in communion with the Universe, allowing her visions to manifest freely, which led her to the realization that everyone and everything were One—time and space were the same reality. What she had experienced in another time in those Sacred Mountains could be relived at any moment. She then noticed that, in like manner, she could transform the heavy energies into subtle ones, to allow the beings of light to come to her aid. And all of this was like an announcement of what was forthcoming. Then suddenly a great light and inner strength became manifest in her and a deep relaxation brought with it sleep and a new dawn.

CRYSTAL CITY

In the midst of her dream she saw herself in a Crystal City, at a Sacred Plaza built especially for meditation and ritual celebrations. In its center rose an altar constructed and placed to watch the precise point and moment of the Sunrise each morning. There was also a small temple where magical ceremonies were carried out. This structure had five windows, three of which were open toward the three energy planes of the initiatory cosmological vision of the mountains of the Sun. The remaining two windows were closed, indicating the energetic frequency of the complements or polarizing currents. These windows were, in fact, the eyes of the Sacred Plaza, and through them one could travel with the Rainbow who, in certain times of the year, manifested itself for this cosmic purpose.

The Crystal City of her vision was a city of the future that radiated Light and Peace. "It is here where once again I am…," Shazadi thought. It wasn't the first time she had visited here, becoming the city of her preference, for the meditative nature of its inhabitants was a natural consequence. She definitely foresaw in her life a period of growth and fulfillment, and already longed for the coming of those moments.

She learned that the most important meditations occurred on those days corresponding with solstices and equinoxes, dates when the sages led their disciples before the altars to initiate them in their Light, where the Sun would alight upon their foreheads and activate their crown centers. In the Crystal City, these places were preserved for only those who sought their spiritual growth and submitted themselves to a rigorous personal discipline. The disciples prepared for powerful solar events, finally becoming initiated, and transcending death through enlightenment with their lives being radically changed upon entering through these gateways of light.

In the Crystal City, all was tenderness and sweetness. One breathed Universal Love in the air and it was possible to enter the womb of the Mother Earth, a divine point where one could establish contact with their inner self and finely tune one's heart with that of the Universe.

Shazadi had lived in the Andes and sought the Crystal City, yet in the physical plane she was unable to find it. Her conscious self placed it in a remote and hidden location in the mountains.

Freedom and Power.

The new dawn found her in better spirits and filled with energy; she felt lighter, less encumbered and strong. The journey to the Sacred Mountains of the Sun had reestablished her link with her warrior life and, in the present moment, she felt that the palace garden constituted the ideal space to further pursue these feelings. Accordingly, Shazadi immersed herself in the art of Sacred Dancing. She was clad in a garment of sky blue color, clear and brilliant as well as very appropriate for this type of dance with sensual and subtle movements of the hips which she managed with much ease, expressing happiness and joy at every turn and maneuver. It was a dance through which priestesses and initiates manifested liberty and beauty.

It was also the perfect moment for Merkaya to set about prying into the Princess's personal belongings in search of further clues and new leads. The Princess had started to behave strangely in the course of the last few days and no longer confided her secrets and thoughts in her. She searched the chamber thoroughly and in one of the drawers of her boudoir, concealed in a small locker, she came upon the letter addressed to her parents, in which Shazadi told them of her intentions as well as her state of pregnancy. Merkaya immediately rearranged everything and immediately went in search of Bernet, who was in his own personal quarters. The servant woman was so excited and confused by the nature of the news she bore, that she entered the chambers of the Prince without knocking or announcing herself. Bernet was unpleasantly startled by the maid's intrusion and promptly demanded explanation. She, however, managed to explain her urgency and breach of etiquette by informing him of the atrocious turn of events. He forgave the impertinence, yet in his mind, not the significance of the news. He felt devastated and immediately set about planning the most terrible revenge for the affront that the lovers had inflicted upon him.

If the elopement was soon to happen, actions should be taken quickly. He instructed the servant to return and keep close watch if the Princess set off to meet her plebeian lover, while he prepared his vengeance.

Shazadi was still in the garden, until she felt the call from her abdomen and realized that she must henceforth be more careful about her health and her diet, for she was now responsible not only for herself but for her future child as well.

She went to the dining room of the palace, helped herself to what she needed in preparation to ride to the gardens on the banks of the Nile.

Merkaya alerted Bernet and he set his plan in motion.

He followed Shazadi cautiously with his eyes, he was blinded with jealousy and felt that life held no sense or meaning. All he wanted was to put an end to this entire matter, yet knew that he would have to act boldly but with caution. His ally, Merkaya, would be the key element in order for his reprisal to be overwhelmingly effective. Hence, he opted to send her alone following in the steps of the Princess.

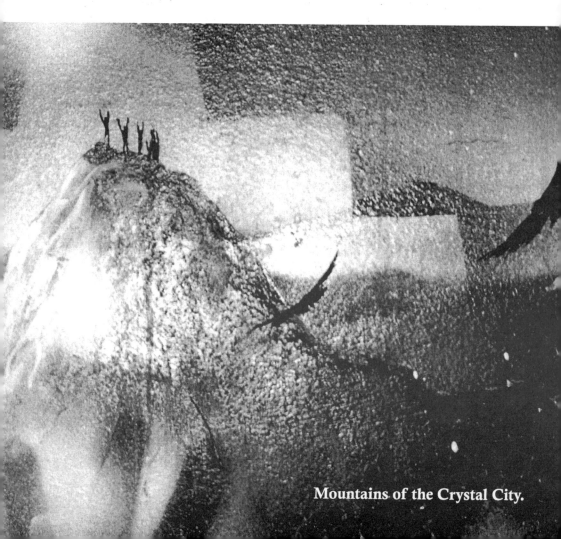

Mountains of the Crystal City.

The ascent of the
Sacred Mountain.

Liberation with
the Birds of Power.

With great attraction and yet little caution, Shazadi and Amrep had fallen into an embrace in the arms of love, entering the realms of inner alchemy. The gardens, decorated with trees and flowering plants formed the divine setting for the lovers, as their bodies came in contact once again blending and sharing their essences as a token of communion and perfection.

Merkaya watched them awaiting to hear further information of their planned escape, but her surprise was great at their unceasing passion and how they embodied the very essence of desire. Not even her hatred and envy would be capable of interfering with their delights, nor impede their bodies from remaining entwined with no intention of stopping. Time passed and the servant woman, having by now already lost control over her own senses, found herself in need of returning to the palace, feeling the heat of passion and more than willing to give herself to whomever should be willing to satisfy her lust.

So it was that on that day Shazadi delighted once again in love, while Merkaya, driven by unbridled desires, experienced the simple magic of orgasm. Although in the practices and conduct of the people matters of sexuality were in most cases restricted or forbidden, this time lust and rampant desire counted more than religion and her pleasure overcame the torment. Nevertheless, love was the ultimate experience which someday Merkaya would have to conquer, for sex alone is but a temporary pleasure, whereas love is the result of the alchemy of the self.

The Princess returned to the palace only at dawn and, as she passed through a corner of the meeting hall, caught a glimpse of Merkaya emerging from Bernet's chambers. She asked herself what she was doing there at these hours. Only then did she fully realize that she should not completely trust her. She proceeded to her quarters while her memory relived the feelings and actions of that unforgettable afternoon, pouring them into verse that expressed her gratitude to life. Love formed part of her creativity, captured and expressed in papyrus, and she felt the urge to record her experiences to use as teachings in future times so that other people who could benefit from her messages.

WAYS

Upon the sea of Love,
I sail intensely.
Discover borders and shores each day,
and attempt to cross them
with the yearning hunger of always feeling Love.
Learning through errors.
Growing in spirit.

Perfecting myself as a person.
Enabled to feel the transparency of each one's mind.
And always a warm smile for reward.
Living, loving, coexisting, feeling.
Sensing, through a simple look,
that united we shall forever be
through one soul, one heart
vibrating to the beat of impacting life.

On this course,
each chooses their own route.
We choose maturity as direction,
struggle as purpose, preferring liberty.
Let us proceed onward, for this is an extensive world.
We shall walk as does the wind:
Strong, eager and determined.

The only formula is to always proceed straightforward.
And remember that life is now beginning.
Needed in this moment
is much Courage and Will to Live.
We are not alone.
Many vessels wrecked in oceans lost,
though bearing different treasures.

Each one in search of a master
who can enable them to navigate in the future,

Vision of the
Crystal City.

The Great Pyramid of Egypt and the Birds of Power

without sinking once more.
Isolated isles, when ocean waves are cast on them
perceive they're not alone,
for waters surrounding them exist,
imparting greater life to their countenance.
Two vessels in the ocean lost
adrift in search of aid,
when meeting, knowing not the reason why,
display a mutual help
that would mountains move.

To each and everyone their own manner and thought.
There are rivers that run for running's sake.
Others reaching hurriedly to encounter the sea.
There are those who still ponder a quiet private life,
forever spent wandering in strange lands.
Many know not their source, nor place of origin.
Yet the motive of their existence
already manifests their worthiness.
And there we find the reason for being.
Each river, with its own current and content of particles,
they carry them on the way to reach somewhere.
Somewhere that is dwelling:
of reflections, self awareness and conflicts.
Yet all and everything can be overcome.
Learning to respect is part of the game.
Learning the game is part of life.
LIVING is our challenge.

When she had finished writing, she felt a desire to reread it and when so doing, felt a shiver; it was another premonition. "There is a part of me speaking from within and it tells me that I set forth upon my way," she thought, feeling that something was about to happen. "I feel a strong sense of loss growing inside me. It seems as if my heart is being braced for something bad to happen. However, I also know that I am receiving help and guidance from my nights of visions have been fantastic experiences in which I attained insight and strength. I am alert and tranquil, gathering courage for when the moment comes. I am a warrior awaiting the coming battle, with many protectors. I know that what is getting closer will not be easy for me, yet I remain trusting," she told herself confidently and then spent a night of uneventful sleep.

On the following morning, Shazadi again awoke to the merry song of one of the small birds that always came chirping to her window, as if biding the Princess good morning.

"How beautiful! You sing like an angel! And a good morning to you as well. How pleasant it is to be woken by your lovely song," said the Princess out loud to the bird, as she rose from her bed.

She changed out of her sleeping clothes into something more suitable for a walk in the gardens. Her breakfast would be served, customarily, upon a long table well-set and decorated.

Merkaya, as always, pretended to serve her submissively, but the servant was alert, expectantly following and spying on her.

Meanwhile, Bernet was adding the final preparations to his plans; he felt extremely tense after discovering that Shazadi was pregnant and that she would soon be eloping. He feared the unpredictable turn of mind that the monarchs might take since Shazadi was their beloved daughter but felt that he would be able to change that situation.

The Monarchs would be arriving sometime in the course of the week, after touring their domains and resolving a series of matters of state. Shazadi normally accompanied them on these visits but this time had preferred to remain behind in order to be close to her lover. The palace had an altogether different atmosphere and feel without the presence of the King and Queen.

The Princess finished her meal and then rode off in the direction of the Pyramids. On the way there, she remembered the moments of bliss and ultimate devotion and surrender of the preceding day spent with Amrep. "The day of our escape is fast approaching," she happily thought to herself.

Merkaya had lost no time and followed in her wake, taking care not to be seen. Once Shazadi's destination was obvious, she detoured past her and arrived at the site of the Pyramids before the Princess.

The two lovers always chose a different spot for their trysts, in order to avoid being detected. Sometimes they met in the gardens by the Nile or at other chosen spots. The Pyramids was one of them.

Merkaya, well concealed, observed the impressive view surrounding her. "I must be able to hear their words," she told herself worriedly.

Shazadi lay stretched on Amrep's lap, while he caressed her pregnant abdomen.

"We depart tomorrow, then? At what time?" she asked him.

"No! Tomorrow is impossible. I sold my parcel of land but won't be paid until later tonight, or tomorrow. We will leave on the day after, very early, before sunrise."

"That's all right! We then have almost two days to prepare. I am ready and wait only for you. If, however, you have a change of mind, send me a message. I should tell you that I have a bad feeling, but also am very happy at the opportunity to build my life with you. Yet I feel that something bad can happen, that can keep us from living together. It is something that I cannot, nor wish to, set from my heart. Do you feel anything in particular?" asked the Princess, as she caressed his hair.

"Yes! I feel both an end and a beginning, a certain unease that I cannot explain. I do not find it easy to describe my feelings as you do, but I think there is something unusual afoot and even considered that we should after all leave early tomorrow. I could make arrangements to be paid at some other time or way. I thought of many other alternatives, but I feel bound up, without any chance to act. When I am in that mind, all I wish is to lie beneath a tree and watch the birds fly by, so as to not do anything. It is a sensation that comes and goes, something blocks my mind and body, leaving me motionless, my muscles numbed with pain."

"Even so, I am prepared to survive, to fight, to defend you and care for the land, the animals and crops. A part of me feels savage and I know that I could live alone in the wilderness, by the river banks or in the deep desert. Where I come from, I grew accustomed to hardship and for me you represent the opposite, so much so that I often feel confused. I appear as a new man inside myself and a different one before you. I regain strength and there is something that nourishes and fills me. Your scent, your look, your touch, everything in you nourishes me. It is sufficient for you to be with me for a few moments for me to feel renewed, loved as I have never been yet within a reality so new and unknown that it scares me at times. The thought of yielding myself to love sometimes fills me with insecurity and I feel the desire to sit under a tree and lose myself in time. Then you arrive, bringing calmness." He tenderly embracing her.

Shazadi felt happy, it was the first time he spoke this way to her, and she then knew that they would be able to communicate very well. Amrep, in the course of his relationship with the Princess, had undergone many changes, especially a greater capacity and ease of self-expression both with her and others. Through it he had also gained a better knowledge of himself, attaining a wider understanding of his own feelings, fears and emotions having embarked upon the path of self awareness.

In contrast, Shazadi was a livelier spirit, possessed of greater knowledge. She would invariably overcome, in due course, her own shortcomings as well as more finely tuning communication between them, fostering their mutual spiritual growth.

"I understand you perfectly," she assured him. "It is a process that you are undergoing and accomplishing within yourself. We all have our own obstacles and unknown issues within us and, as we get to know more of ourselves, we likewise learn to naturally overcome them with ease, gaining greater insight of ourselves. I believe that life begins when we become willing to explore, in all its fullness, who we are."

She went on. "It is impressive how we tend to be distant from ourselves. We spend an entire existence repeating and reliving the legacy bequeathed to us by our grandparents, in turn through our parents, associated to habits from our own present day cultural such as experiences, tastes, needs, etc. We learn to live each day led by the goal of recreating, being good in order to achieve the recognition of others as well as of ourselves. From the day of our birth, we enter upon the wheel of life where we struggle for our survival, always having things to do and the unremitting need to HAVE. We struggle to obtain a livelihood, to attain a respectable place within the community. Then, one day we become mothers and fathers, with a greater need of material goods. At that point, HAVING becomes the priority of OUR ENTIRE LIFE."

"I agree with you. How good it is to hear your words; they sound sweet to my ears," said Amrep, embracing her and caressing her long and shiny locks.

Shazadi wanted to continue speaking, she was enthralled by spiritual themes and felt increasingly inspired through being in a Place of Power as were the Pyramids. So she went on:

"You know, these days I have been writing much about love, you inspire me to write. At some time, I would like you to hear my poetry. At times I feel that it is not myself who writes them, it seems as if there is someone else within me and the messages that I am receiving are notices, harbingers of the future. Before knowing you, I had a revelation and then knew that there was someone special... allowing it all to flow..." she said, emotionally overtaken.

"I want to see you always strong and, well-disposed, I wish to care for you as well as for our child," Amrep told her resolutely that during the last few days he was more open and eager. After knowing that she bore his child, something in him had changed. "This is all so beautiful, I love your words. I want so much to know your poetry. I believe it is amazing that a person like you has the gift to express herself with such wisdom," he spoke earnestly and emotionally.

Shazadi then, at that place and moment, wrote these words for him:

BEING/HAVING

WE HAVE MUCH MORE THAN WHAT WE THINK.
WE ARE MUCH MORE THAN WHAT WE FEEL.
WE CAN BE SO MUCH MORE THAN WHAT WE IMAGINE.
WE HAVE THE PRESENT MOMENT.
WE ARE THE PRESENT MOMENT.
WE CAN ACHIEVE A FULFILLED LIFE.

LIFE

In this intermittent process of life, we find ourselves lost in the sea.
We are those sailors in need of the skies to fly,
of the earth to survive and the sea to find freedom.
Clouds gather in our thoughts.
The latter crushed by a pain that evaporates in seconds.
Each particle materializing
and expanding in the world of survival.
Living in a world so distant from a human being! Surviving.
Night star, magic that touches us, illuminating the sky.
Nature – Natural Life.
Living in the Sea of Love.
The heart aflame becomes a blaze.
And that love causes to grow.
Lightly touching breeze, with it bringing so much peace.

Shazadi felt connections with other Beings who were present and further wrote:

WE ARE MUCH MORE THAN WE CAN IMAGINE

We grant ourselves what we deserve and what we don't.
It is necessary to believe that we can BE more.
We project on life in an exalted manner, with vivacity and happiness.
We deserve more.
Let us project beyond the limits imposed by society,
and we will be ourselves
in every instant throughout our entire life.
The present is important,
it becomes a challenge to live each moment in soul and body,
breathing with the heart.
For, if that were it, we can use the lungs and heart at the same time.

Merkaya remained observing them for a few hours. She had managed to make her way close enough to overhear what she needed to. "I shall immediately return to the palace and inform my Lord Bernet that they plan to depart in two days time." She said to herself, quickly returning. "I have nothing of further interest to listen to and if I remain here I shall go mad, I don't want to witness their love making, it disturbs me," she thought, besought with rage and envy.

Shazadi felt the need to continue speaking. There were many invisible beings around her and in that moment, time and space seemed split apart. The Magical World of Egypt lay open before them. The Princess experienced parallel worlds that combined with all that she believed in. It was the world of beauty and pleasure. WHAT THE HUMAN BEING IS!

Shazadi thus taught Amrep to never feel lost, or to base his security and self-confidence upon the thought or presence of her or someone else, because he could never find outside of himself the conviction he needed. He had to understand that all lay within him and that his beloved could not be his shelter and safe haven through the rest of life. He would have to learn to walk on his own, even when living with her. He had to discover himself and allow his divine essence to flow to the surface. Amrep listened to all she spoke, needing this moment and these messages to pursue his path. Amrep had long ago enfolded her in his embrace, tenderly caressing her belly, and the silent nodding of his head denoted his understanding and acceptance of the Princess' words, as well as a feeling of satisfaction and contentment at these messages of the soul.

Meanwhile, Merkaya had reached the palace and went quickly to Bernet's chambers.

"My Lord, I come bearing news," she told him, panting out of breath.

"Speak quickly," he told her, in a tone of contempt and annoyance.

"The escape will take place on the day after tomorrow. They will set off at daybreak," Merkaya uttered rapidly to ingratiate herself with the irritable Prince.

"Are you certain of what you say, did you hear exactly what they said?" Bernet asked, his tone now denoting a hint of worry.

"Absolutely, My Lord, I heard very well. The Princess wanted to depart sooner, but it seems that he has sold his parcel of land and will only receive payment tomorrow night. Only after that will they leave," she paused, then suddenly she dared to ask, very tensely, "What are you planning to do?."

"His death will take place tomorrow. We will wait until Shazadi arrives for her usual tryst and then I shall send mounted soldiers there. I want it to be a quick death. You will let me know the moment she leaves the palace. I shall ready my men right now, nothing must fail, and...," here Bernet's voice faltered, "and yet, in spite of everything, I love that woman," he said, his voice now showing a hint of suffering.

"Very well, My Lord," said the servant woman, bowing her head and leaving the room.

Bernet felt very distraught by Merkaya's news. "Yes, it will be tomorrow," he said out loud, as though to reassure himself.

Sometime later, when the Princess arrived back at the palace, she immediately felt a shudder raking her body. Everything appeared somber and shrouded in a dense energy. There was, undoubtedly, something very strange and foreboding looming about. She went down the corridor, close to Bernet's quarters to see if she could find something out. "I do not know what is wrong here, but the energy is obscure," she told herself with absolute conviction.

However, she saw nor heard anything, no lights were lit so Shazadi withdrew to her chamber to rest. Before going to sleep, she reviewed her writings, read her letter to her parents and was overtaken by emotion, but her decision was made and she would stand by it. Ready to lay down, she returned her pages to the same drawer where they had lain before. Again, a feeling of foreboding came over her. "I'm sure that something not good is afoot," she thought. Seeking to assuage her uneasiness, she resorted to immersing herself in deep meditation. She performed her breathing, slowly gained a hold of herself. Leaving her mind in a tranquil state, her body relaxed and she found herself within an extremely disconcerting inner vision:

There were many horses and she, running among them, was overcome by the sensation that something terrible was about to happen. Amrep appeared and the horses moved close to him, many armed warriors surrounded him. Then, a sensation of peacefulness enveloped her.

Finally, the Princess entered upon deep sleep.

While all these events unfolded, Amrep, after parting ways with Shazadi, had slowly made his way back home, arriving there at a late hour. A sense of sadness had crept over him, a sense of grief weighed heavily on his chest. In the slumber on his modest cot, he thought at length about Shazadi's words. This nurtured him and he felt more at ease. Seconds later, he too was fast asleep.

Back at the palace, Bernet unceasingly reviewed the plan in his mind: "It must be perfect, there can be no traces. She must never suspect me, at any moment. My hands must remain absolutely clean."

Merkaya, on the other hand, lay in her room, beside herself with joy: "How good that it will all be over tomorrow; I will then have the pleasure of witnessing a Princess in ruins," she sang to herself.

And the next day arrived... Shazadi woke up feeling tense. She had slept well, yet awakened overcome by the same foreboding of doom that had hounded her some hours before. In his hut, Amrep awoke with a similar feeling. He performed his prayers, but the oppressive feeling in his chest did not go away. At the other end of it all, Bernet woke up, as did Merkaya, feeling light and happy each after their own fashion, for today was very important to them both. They were about to destroy of the happiness of the two lovers.

Shazadi passed from her chamber into the garden to meditate. After taking a seat on one of the benches close to the water fountain, she began her prayers, asking for enlightenment and protection during the coming events.

In his own home in the village, Amrep readied his few belongings, yet the weight upon his chest showed no sign of letting up. The only relief came from thinking of Shazadi, at all times present in his mind and heart. "I miss her. How good it was to see each other yesterday and knowing in a few hours' time we shall be together again. I feel a mixture of fear and desire, but it will go away as soon as I am beside her," he reflected, seeking to alleviate his tension.

Bernet, on his part, had everything organized and ready. He had issued the orders to the palace warriors and all waited for his signal to set the plan in motion.

Merkaya, the fourth player in the drama, seemed the only one carelessly happy. She was bursting with excitement and eager expectation. During the morning, she prepared and packed her belongings. For when it was all over, she would vanish along with her foully earned reward, jewelry and other valuables. "I want to build a life which is mine alone, full of abundance..... uuuulalala," she sang, full of self assurance."

Shazadi, her prayers completed, dressed herself in her finest and most becoming garments: a white dress of finely spun lightweight material, which vibrated and danced with the breeze. Her loose black hair created a dazzling effect to her presence. She was delicately yet noticeably perfumed, and as always, very beautiful. The Princess was endowed with a natural beauty and elegance; large, dark chestnut-brown eyes, a generously sensuous smiling mouth, light colored skin, and the stature of a Goddess. She radiated joy and happiness at every step, and her inner beauty, cast freely and unbound, made her all the more irresistible. She was a woman longed-for and desired. Yet she showed no interest in anyone of her social class, for they were generally ambitious and presumptuous, flaunting and abusing their material belongings while showing no interest or recognition of the Spiritual world. Such persons always regarded themselves as the center of everything and, in meetings and events the Princess felt detached and uninterested, considering the lot of them as empty individuals.

Amrep had also donned his finest: he wore brown sandals, a white tunic similar in texture to that of his beloved's, a gift from her, and was soon ready for their meeting. At that moment, in a different place, Shazadi simultaneously straddled her steed and set off at a gallop, watching if she was being followed, yet saw no one.

Merkaya, however, who had been attentively watching her every move, immediately informed Bernet of her departure from palace.

"I am ready, today is a great day," were the words of the Prince, as he gave the fateful order to his warriors.

Merkaya remained in her quarters, anxiously awaiting the outcome of Bernet's revenge. He, in turn, was meeting privately with his troop. They seemed equipped more for war than for the murder of an unarmed victim. They bore spears, swords, shields, heavy armor and were mounted battle steeds displaying combat saddlery and harnessing. All total there were forty warriors, trained to win or die. These were the men entrusted by Bernet with the mission of Amrep's death. Their cowardice and insecurity showed, among other things, in the number of soldiers chosen to ambush and attack one defenseless man. That was the way Bernet devised his scheme in order for his hands to not be personally stained or blamed for the attract, nor the Princess suspecting him. If that were to happen, all would be lost.

The horsemen set off in the direction of the gardens by the banks of the Nile, led by their best scout. Bernet planned to make his personal appearance after the accomplished fact, accompanied by another detachment, arriving late to effect a pretense of defending Shazadi and her, by then dead, lover. The initial ambush party covered their faces so that the Princess would not recognize any of them even though she never actually had any contact with palace soldiers. Bernet did not want the slightest possibility that would link him to being the mastermind behind the murder.

Shazadi had by now arrived at Amrep's side, dismounted and embraced him in the grips of passion. He was in need of this loving, for he thought of her all morning and felt disconsolate and distressed. Yet her presence soon changed that.

"I have thought of you so much, your absence weighed heavily on my spirit," he spoke in a broken voice, as he held her in his arms.

"As have I," she told him, "for something is amiss and hangs threateningly about. Yesterday, as I entered the palace, I was overcome by a strong feeling of danger, followed by a vision of mounted men pursuing you... and then suddenly, I saw no more. I am in anguish about this, I prayed much and feel that we should depart tomorrow at all costs. We cannot wait any longer," Shazadi entreated him with her eyes firmly fixed on his.

Amrep was a tall, strong, well-built man, with tanned complexion, black hair thrown back reveling a manly countenance with good-looking features, almond-shaped eyes of dark brown and an engaging smile. He had powerful broad hands, large enough to cover Shazadi's delicate abdomen. He was, in short, handsome and virile, and as such, the women of the village felt attracted to him. Aware of the impression he made on them, he occasionally allowed himself to win their hearts and favors. However, he felt very different with Shazadi, in a way that helped him to live better. At the same, nevertheless, he was essentially a person of simple and humble origin, dedicated to nature, the care of animals and charitable to his fellows.

Shazadi was willing to live with a man. She had not necessarily gone about seeking someone to share her moments, experiences or feelings with. But Amrep had given her attention, tenderness, pleasure, and wanted to live with her. All these factors had brought Shazadi to the decision to commit to this relationship. Today marked the sixth month of their relationship, hence their mutual decision to dress in white, symbolizing the purity of souls and heart. They formed a beautiful couple. The lovers again embraced in the warmth of the moment.

Amrep then stepped back and, from the shade of a great tree, stood gazing admiringly at the Princess, her beauty and femininity, his look explored every part of her body until his eyes reached hers and remained fixed. Their eyes locked in a gaze that overflowed with affection and tenderness.

Their mutual reverie was abruptly broken by the sound of galloping horses approaching. Shazadi shook and spoke to Amrep:

"It's not possible, can it be that my visions are coming true? They are coming this way, they are soldiers and are here now, they must be after you. But you are innocent, you've committed no crime, what can they accuse you of?" she said, in a beseeching voice, feeling on the verge of fainting.

Amrep looked at her, fear now showing in his eyes, as if bidding farewell and started to run. The Princess fell to the ground, caught in desperation, she rose almost immediately unwilling to accept that harm could come to her lover. She ran after him. Seconds became eternities, she was gripped by anguish and desperation, her chest heaved and ached, her breath failing. The warriors were already upon him, she could see that they were armed exactly as she has seen in her visions.

"Why all this? What is Amrep guilty of to be hunted down like this? I know he is innocent of everything!" Shazadi thought and spoke frantically, running in his direction.

It all happened very swiftly, a matter of seconds allowing no time for thought, speech or action. The Princess watched the horses, more than she did the riders, and heard the thunder of their hooves. They were so fast and strong, impossible to withstand or to escape from, more so in the case of two unarmed people. "How cowardly, to thus pursue an innocent man," was Shazadi's last thought before the imminent outcome. A spear flew toward Amrep and struck him in the chest. Shazadi stumbled and fell. As if from a distant vision, she heard her voice screaming a long and endless "NOOOO!"

She somehow regained her feet and ran to Amrep's side, in time to comfort his final moments. He was mortally wounded, his life quickly leaving him in an abundant pouring of blood. The Princess vainly attempted to staunch the deadly flow with her hands, even with kisses. Amrep could no longer speak and only looked at her. Shazadi, mustering the last of her strength, pulled the spear from his broken breast. The gaping wound was large and deep. In her despair, she realized there was nothing she could do to save him, yet, in one last hopeful effort she covered her lover's body with her own and held him tightly, attempting to stop the final drops of his life from escaping.

"Don't leave, my love, I want to live with you. I love you," she muttered in her impotence. The last of his strength gave way and, continuing to gaze into her eyes, he perished. His spirit flew to eternity and the Universe came to a standstill for Shazadi. She was in shock. So great was her pain that she lost consciousness, knowing that her dreams had now ended.

"My love, my life and dreams have also perished. What will I do without you?" The words emerged from her after awhile, calmly, unarmed, without the will to cry or scream. The world had lost sense, they had murdered her loved one. Then, a though, a faint reminder that she was still alive, crossed her mind fleetingly: "How can there be so much evil?"

From a distance, Bernet had observed everything. He lay waiting for the exact moment to make his appearance. He was happy, or perhaps only content. "How good that this game has finally ended, from now on the Princess will be mine," he thought, radiantly. He then began to make his approach, drew close to the Princess, dismounted, leaned toward her and held out his hand to her. The Princess silently accepted it.

The warriors that formed part of Bernet's entourage, the other party of masked murderers having hastily departed upon the appearance of the Prince, lifted Amrep's corpse and carried it to the river bank. Shazadi mounted her horse with a hint of difficulty, but did not weep and quickly gained hold of herself. Bernet followed her but kept close by her side. The soldiers unceremoniously flung the body of her lover into the waters and she silently spoke a prayer to his memory. At no moment showing the state of shock which still gripped her, she gazed at the river waters carrying away the dead body of her beloved, whom she would never see again. She made a slightly imperceptible movement with her hands resembling the shape of a heart and likewise unnoticed, cast a parting kiss.

With an indescribable pain wrenching her bosom, as though her heart had been torn out of her, she returned to the palace in silence. Bernet watched her closely, but did not dare to intrude upon her grief. Once there, he escorted her to the doorway of her chambers and finally spoke his first and last words of the day to her:

"It is best that you rest. If you need anything, I am at your service." He then kissed her on the cheek and departed.

"Thank you," she responded, closed the door and collapsed on her bed.

Merkaya watched from a hiding place and as soon as Bernet left, ran to the Princess's room.

"My Lady, what has happened? Can I be of assistance? I can bring water and a remedy to calm you," Merkaya said, almost screaming in her attempt at false pretense.

Shazadi said nothing, took the water, drank all of it and a short while later she was asleep.

Merkaya went to Bernet's chambers to hear of the events.

"My Lord..." she announced her presence at his doorway.

"Yes? Oh, its you. Enter. I will now give you your pay and you may depart going to a very distant place. I have no wish for any evidence to remain," he told her dryly and handed her the promised reward.

"Thank you, My Lord," she managed to utter, and hastily, as well as joyfully, left his presence. She gathered her belongings and disappeared, to an unknown destination, never to be seen again.

Bernet celebrated with relish for the remainder of the day, in the privacy of his chamber he made no attempt to disguise his gloating happiness. "Now, 'tis but a matter of time before I make the Princess mine," he reminded himself time and again. Few in the palace were aware of the goings-on, for the return of the monarchs was due in a few days' time and courtiers and servants were busily engaged preparing their welcome. All were busy, no one knew or noticed the Princess's bereavement.

Shazadi, in her dreams, visited the Crystal City:

She was ceremonially ushered by Beings of Light. They indicated her to kneel and she understood that she was undergoing an initiation. The Sun alighted upon her third eye and the Beings of light formed a circle around her while illuminating her with rays like those of the rainbow. Everything lay in a state of flux and intermingling. She realized that they were cleansing her heart of the pain it bore. They gradually dispersed the energies of lower density and illuminated with the Sacred Fire (Willka Nina) and cleansed every fiber of her heart until all sadness and discomfort had vanished.

Everything had been transmuted and Shazadi felt lighter and calmer. They then performed a surgery in her abdomen, for she had miscarried the child during the emotional shock. When cleansing her womb, Shazadi perceived the Being leaving her matrix. At the moment of bidding farewell, her son transformed into a naked man. He kissed her face and went on his way. The Princess had been healed, she was renewed and stayed for the remainder of the night within this Center of Light. She was at peace, the pains had vanished. She breathed Love and Tranquility. She remained asleep.

When Shazadi opened her eyes she felt at ease and calm. Rising from her bed, she looked out her window, the birds sang beautiful songs. She gazed upon nature and performed her prayers. Returning to her bed, she was suddenly paralyzed by the sight of the sheets soaked with blood and a fetus lying among the folds. She let out a cry and, almost immediately remembered what had taken place. She removed the sheets and tenderly wrapped the fetus to later bury him in the palace gardens, after which she wept, but not of pain but rather of sadness at all that had taken place.

Suddenly, a servant girl appeared, set to perform the cleaning chores of her chamber.

"Who are you? Where is Merkaya?," asked the Princess.

"My name is Linya, I am replacing the other servant woman. She has gone off, apparently to get married. At least, this is what is said among the palace servants. I have been working here for a few months, helping to organize the welcome banquet for their Majesties, your parents, who are due to arrive the day after tomorrow. Now, I have been ordered to serve you," explained the girl as she went about her work.

Shazadi watched her and listened to her words with restraint. "How odd that Merkaya never spoke to me about an impending marriage and that she would depart so suddenly and hastily. Yet another strange happening. Could it be that she is involved in the murder of my lover and the death of my child? I shall get to the bottom of this," she thought, with sadness.

Through the remainder of that morning, the Princess sheltered herself in the garden meditating. She also devoted part of her time to writing what her feelings dictated. She gave instructions that she was not to be interrupted, as she immersed herself in profound reflections.

Willka Nina - Sacred Fire,
Master of Alchemy.

"It is in the simplicity of the moment and the receptivity of the heart that spiritual peace is found." Shazadi silently reminded herself. Then she wrote:

REFLECTIONS

In life, I have learned to face determined events, to analyze and overcome obstacles. At times I seek a goal that I know not the nature of and imagine it as something new, a different world. I have already known disenchantment many times with people as my teachers. My concept of life at times confuses me, it transforms itself into an interminable conflict that begins at some given point and never do I know when it will end. At times it grows and begins to prevail and confound everything, endlessly branching out and eventually becoming unbearable.

When that climax is reached, I search for a way to escape from myself, weep, disappear, depart, seclude myself, launch into unknown and unwise doings, even insanity. But then I mange to re-identify with nature, the birds, the Moon, the Stars, the Sun... and this does good to me, it gives me inspiration and desire to live. I am able to feel again and breathe clean air, while the sky covers my body with its light and power. There are other moments in which I feel alone, with doubts, conflicts, longing for my loved one. Then, I become immersed in my reflections... and reflections...

In that state of mind, Shazadi spent the entire day in the garden, until the coming of night.

Solar Initiation.

Illuminating with the Sacred Fire (Willka Nina) and transmutations.

Receiving the
Cosmic Stone.

SENSATIONS

One look makes me remember.
The body trembles.
Wind that strikes and provokes.
A hot night. I am cold.

I feel the lack of your eyes.
I search in every place,
but find only in thoughts.
There is no satisfaction.

I yearn for your loving.
I have need of finding
a place of ease.
I wish to live!

The Moon rises spontaneously.
Makes me feel happy.
I hear songs of love,
that penetrate, beating and beating in my ears.

My lips hunger.
They mouth your name.
Time passes, yet another day has gone.
Emotions become mixed.

I feel the scent
of that night serene.
I feel cold.
My body yearns for yours.

CONFUSIONS

On days confused, explanations seem more difficult to seek out; although I can live, breathe, feel awareness of my body and its limits... and pensive remain. I come upon exclamations, interrogations and attempt to find a way out. But I fail to understand people, creepy creatures, irrational, momentary, without a reason for being, unconscious animals, figures clad in flesh and often lacking heart.

The night is everywhere illuminated, there are lights in all places. I seek the stars, they give me energy, they help me to find the human side in that which lacks life. I then travel in each one of them and I gather piecemeal, the parts that make up my body. And I perceive that I am one of them. My eyes sparkle before the presence of happiness, I feel Love, I Love Life; and a delicious fire rises and takes charge over me. I am floating, I am transported to a place of beauty, where I feel free. And we are all akin and true when allowing our Divine Essence to Live. A lovely light surges from the hearts of everyone, and unites us with great strength, turning us into one soul and only Self, restoring the desire to grow and live moments of happiness and joy for all...

Reality has now suddenly returned and caught me unawares in the garden. There are many persons here and, at the same time, no one or anything has any worthiness. What remain are the moments of the heart, spontaneous and condensed. I feel cold, what is happening?... darkness.

Shazadi retired to her chamber after almost an entire day of meditation and found herself feeling lighter and less overcome by grief. She had sought to understand her outer and inner self and find a balance. Hence, in the extent of her reflections, sensations and confusions she turned to nature for help and healing, while carrying out an in-depth inner process of self understanding. She sought to reach the core of intimacy in the present–the current difficult moment of her life. Yet, once in bed, she lay back and quickly fell asleep, being as she was, in no small need of rest. In her dreams, she once again traveled to that mysterious and magical city of the people of the Sun, the Crystal City:

Shazadi was transported to the Crystal City, she felt at peace, surrounded by the animal creatures of power of the mountains, whom she revered, and jointly participated in an initiatory ceremony. She was already familiar with the process. The Puma represented cognizance and strength and it was him who conducted her walk through the Crystal City. The Hummingbird fluttered about her body and touched her third eye; this bird represented Love. The Cosmic Serpent who represented rebirth was wrapped around her entire body and at every instant reflected lights and shades of many different colors, the most intense being violet, the color of transmutation. Shazadi herself reflected and shone in different colors with the moment, she absorbed this energy, balancing all her *chakras*, or primary energy centers.

Then a Rainbow appeared as if protecting the entire Crystal City and illuminating the sites of meditation where many priests were present. Next, appeared the Llama, who represented prosperity. Lastly, she made out the presence of the Kondor, the symbol of Liberation and Freedom. It flew, very elegantly gliding over the City, displaying a plumage of black and white and a wingspan of three meters. Touching ground close to Shazadi, it invited her to ride throughout the entire region. To say the least, the Princess felt fulfilled to the utmost, experiencing the expansion of Freedom. She felt a sensation that this was taking place over a period measured in years, for everything was so profound and intense that Shazadi felt as if she were floating in space and time.

The Princess was transformed and the events of the death of her beloved ones were relegated to a now distant past. At that very moment she caught sight of someone observing her from afar. She immediately

recognized an ancient soul sharing a common bond. So strong was this feeling of integration, that she walked toward this person to see if it was someone of importance in her life. The encounter was sealed with a loving embrace. Shazadi had found a beloved being, the Messenger of the Mountains, a mysterious being of this City of Magic and Power, where the elements merge to form the highest frequencies of light radiating their energy to the world. The two eternal lovers, from a time long past, had again recognized and found each other and celebrated the ages-long encounter in a union of peace and liberation.

When she woke, Shazadi felt as though she had no body because of the sensation of lightness that pervaded her. She wrote a poem placing in it "words that she would like to hear:"

WORDS THAT I WANTED TO HEAR

Songs of love to scare the pain.
A sweet word. Friendly advice.
The language of rain.
The ocean waves breaking.
Words that can speak in the language of the heart.
Capable of feeling all of the sincerity
and the truth in each letter, in every sound.
A hello followed by a smile warmly greeting.
As the dawning Sun
with a brilliance reflected everywhere.
To hear messages coming from the Sky
and share with energy.
Much Love to be distributed
in forms of sound.

The days passed rapidly, Shazadi's parents arrived and the great welcoming banquet took place. The Princess wanted to be with them for, in a way, their presence made her feel secure.

Bernet availed himself of the circumstances to become closer to Shazadi. She accepted his company and together they strolled and walked about, conversing of this and that. The monarchs were satisfied with this relationship. The Princess had told only her mother of the recent happenings. The Queen gave her daughter support and reassurance, but advised her to rebuild her life at Bernet's side. And this Shazadi tried to do, but she felt a barrier in her heart. She was closed to him as lover, though not as friend. Nevertheless, over time, Bernet succeeded in obtaining what he wanted. The date for the wedding was set.

Months passed since Amrep's death and the Princess had regained strength and found the peace of her soul, receiving much support from the spiritual world. Every night, the Beings of Light worked alongside her, leading her on the paths of liberation and awareness of her inner strength. The encounters with the Mysterious Being of the Crystal City became more frequent and they had consecrated their love in that realm of the astral world and *Akashic* Records. The experiences in the magic realm were of such intensity for her that when Shazadi performed her meditations in the palace garden, she was capable of identifying the scent and aroma of her timeless lover. All of this contributed to help lift her pain and grief. But the presence of the Mysterious Being sped the process of her peace, finding calmness and serenity.

Shazadi again became secure in herself and decided to continue working with the women of the villages, helping them in tasks of self awareness, growth and releasing toward spiritual freedom. Everyone prospered in harmony and peace.

Shazadi and Bernet were married one year after the events surrounding the death of Amrep. She remained exuberantly lovely as always. In the course of the years, she had achieved a spiritual elegance and life gave her two children. The Princess had become a loving mother, devoted to her family.

Time passed and Shazadi found herself once again carrying a child in her. Yet this pregnancy proved very complicated for her, to the point that she was bedridden for almost the entire nine months.

The delivery was so difficult, that the child was stillborn. Shazadi, however, lived for some weeks more, but she was stricken with illness and her body eventually gave out and she passed away–twenty years after Amrep's death. Though in the final stages of her illness, the Princess had written:

MY SOUL AND MY HEART

So many are the lives that make of us one soul being, that all is transcendental. We are much more than we can imagine, we are beings so great in the sacred path, that the transformations always come at the precise moment when we open our hearts.

The story of "losing someone" does not exist, because in the spiritual world we never lose anything or anyone. In the spiritual world what counts is you, with your love and inner strength. We are all capable of attaining it, but we have forgotten how.

My heart lies in a lovely moment of openness and receptivity, growing much and depending solely upon myself to open further. In this moment, external matters count for little. Everything passes: the pain, sadness and the want of understanding. Now what is most important is to focus on my heart. Suffering exists no more. I open like a flower that every morning exhales its aroma sharing that scent with other flowers; and the soul, in all its purity, becomes larger and greater, filling with light, illuminating everyone and everything around it.

"You are a flower of such importance that the Universe conspires for you to be remembered for the eventfulness of your life. YOU ARE MORE THAN ALL OF THIS, YOU CAN CROSS THAT PATH OF THE JOURNEY OF YOUR EVOLUTION WITH SERENITY, BY PLACING YET MORE BELIEF UPON THE PROCESS OF YOUR OVERALL VOYAGE," my spiritual friends tell me.

The hindrances and resistance that we place in the way of everything we see with our eyes, do not allow the internal motion of the heart, or the expansion of the soul, to happen. We must leave these obstacles, and the placing of them, behind. For they only serve to complicate us and at any and all levels cause further inner suffering. It is like swimming against the current but we must allow the growth of the inner motion of the heart through love and gentleness, until pain and suffering are gone and everything unnecessary is left behind. I touch my heart with love, I am one with it, my soul expands, growing to become one in pleasure, liberty and happiness. I love my own self and I am great, I see the light within me, light that grows and illuminates wherever I am bound.

Shazadi´s body was cremated and her ashes scattered in the same river where Amrep's body had once been flung. She died never having known the reason for Amrep's death nor of those involved in the perpetration of this crime.

DISCOVERINGS

In the profound transparency of your eyes,
I find tenderness and vibration, flaming fire.
Here I am and at the same time I am not.
I come and go in fractions of a second,
Transport myself in a manner spontaneous.
Live, breathe, I am loving!
Passion surrounds me from all sides,
The air I breathe leaves me weightless.
Vegetation conceals a fertile soil,
Such as we hide a lovely heart,
Covered, overgrown with contagious impurities of survival.
What to do! Discover others emotions.
There is still time for reconciliation.
Time to navigate and sail, time to hunt and be hunted.
The importance is discovering the function of each organ,
Every part that composes our body.
What to do inside four walls?
Think, find oneself, or suffocate?
I hear distant voices, the sound of doors closing.
Another winter morning passing.
Day of calm, hectic life.

What remains is what we really are.
And what are we, who are we?
The doubt remains amidst so much assuredness.

With Love, Shazadi.

Andean Kondor.

THE LOVE

Sensations mix and mingle,
like clouds in the sky.
One song obscures another,
within a difficult concurrence of volumes.
An intenseness of taste,
reappears stronger,
and deletes what is past,
"that" which grounds and premise is lacking.
Already, a fault, a precious "lack" appears.
A want –this one touching and moving.
The need of finding,
moments such as that one
never forgotten.
At the bottom of it all we are together
and both together masters of the same gaze,
that carries meaning with it.
Emotions, doubts, desires.
We form part of a whole body,
which makes us wise
and belonging to a word,
many times difficult to voice,
but that feeds upon our blood
and our soul.
It brings us closer to our true "I,"
further purifying that which is the purest
in the human existence:
THE LOVE

ALWAYS STRIVING,
NEVER ENDING.

PART TWO

New life,
new path
to the light.

MEXICO, 21ST CENTURY

The tides and currents of life led to Shazadi's rebirth in another land of Power—Mexico. It was to be in this new life that she would discover many of the great secrets of her existence. The Mayan Sages created in this land many cities, with palaces and temples. Yet more than a few were forgotten and others partially destroyed by the ideologies of the newer so-called civilizations.

In this new experience, Shazadi became acquainted with a number of enlightened persons, yet there were many questions that remained unanswered for the sake of easing her soul. Toward the end of the fourth year of that "new" century, great changes in the world were foretold and this brought new hope into her life.

During the December Solstice, she gathered, in the center of a retreat with other people to celebrate the advent of this new era, thus achieving a fraternity of beings who did not know one another, with the purpose that all could share the ideal of a new rebirth. That day, she met some elders, and they, as if intuitively aware of her needs, offered to her a number of stories and messages which she accepted with the same gratefulness of one receiving a present from parents eager to provide protection. This particular site of spiritual retreat, were arranged astronomically which, in turn, rendered homage to some of the ancient centers of the Maya people who possessed cosmological knowledge of the heavens and their relation with the earth. There were waterfalls cascading over ornamental fountains with fish and green areas replete with beautiful flowers. It was a place where the spiritual was part of its natural structure, a center of care for the body and the soul. That day, Shazadi learned that there existed persons with very strong desires to maintain a life unhampered by recurring daily frustrations.

Learning to live in the moment and sharing what little or much they had, was the mission of the initiates, as well as a representation of the dynamic Universe itself. Whoever escaped or abstained from this interaction, would find only suffering and desolation.

In addition to decorative fountains, there was also an artificial lake in which Shazadi took the opportunity to dive into its crystalline waters and

The Sacred Kondor.

feel the effect of conscious cleansing that the liquid element offered. When the Being integrates within the beauty of life, events flow naturally with greater ease. Everything was part of the apprenticeship and learning was a bastion or stronghold necessary for setting life on the right track of the path of light, with the sole aim of satisfaction and equilibrium of action.

Shazadi made use of every available opportunity to free herself from mental and physical burdens. One fine day, walking in the forest, she received the call from a great tree. In response, she approached and embraced it, feeling it communicating in her body and soul. It was a matter of tuning and transmission of natural experiences and forces that involved unique scenarios from many times and places. This was such a special contact that it caused Shazadi to experience fulfillment and purification of many genetic burdens, that had on a given occasion even compromised her own blood. On the following day, when returning to the forest to visit her tree friend, she found that it was no longer there, for it had been cut down. She then realized, with much sadness, that this great tree had already known what its fate held in store, and for that reason had decided, on that previous day, to create a nexus in space and time with her.

Many changes began to come about for Shazadi; so many that one time, when at the beach, she felt her integration with the sea and immersed herself in the limitless ocean. Its waters, with their powerful forces, cleansed her of her fears and some ailments as well. The understanding that a single drop and the complete ocean both bear the same essence was a gift from the Universe. She likewise learned that illness and health are two sides of the same coin, wisdom of a lifetime in which to cultivate health and with it happiness. Illness then transforms into a mere messenger heralding that things will improve when we implement attitudes of acceptance and changing nature. Only through becoming conscientious of these truths, can we enlighten humanity.

Over a period of four months, Shazadi followed the inner way gaining knowledge of her body and the therapies to heal it. She found it necessary to enter into her blood stream and circulatory system, in search of the key to the respiratory techniques required to overcome physical as well as mental difficulties which might present themselves in life. She learned that many family and social conflicts exercise powerful effects on individuals, and if they modify their thought patterns and actions, the cure manifests itself as a consequence of their quest for equilibrium.

Prior to this gathering, Shazadi had been living moments of dissatisfaction, within a routine that cut short her possibilities of growth and attainment of true authenticity. She decided to immediately act upon it. As a Pilgrim, she reached the Initiatory Centers of the great Pyramid of Chichen Itza, to pursue the path of the Sun. In this Site of Power she acquired first-hand proof that the Sages activated their inner Suns and that, in the process of great ceremonies, were able to speak with the stars. For Shazadi, the discovery of this world of magic and fascination represented a great opportunity. In her practices, she performed physical exercises and meditations for the purpose of freeing herself from karmic fetters and ties. These meditations, along the shamanic path led her to states of ecstasy and out of this world connections.

In one of these voyages of timelessness, she again journeyed to the Crystal City **and there had another encounter with the Messenger of the Mountains, the mysterious being who had so often appeared to her.**

> **"You are the Woman who has been present many times in the course of my lives. Now we meet once more. I offer you this gift to keep forever," he said tenderly and assuring, as he extended it to her.**

> **"What is it?" she asked with curiosity. When receiving it, she could feel it was a stone of Cosmic Origin.**

Shazadi learned to utilize this powerful instrument to visualize her requests and petitions, and to make them come true. Her desires and wishes materialized. One of these was the wish to integrate wholly with this mysterious being, for their connections were not only of the soul but of the body as well. When again face to face with each other, she realized that the energy of communion and alchemy had been prepared for them to meet once more in this plane full of insight and keenness, in which the sum of times freely merged. The communion of this love was crowned in the Crystal City, which was the ultimate expression of harmony and beauty. The choreography of its rugged mountains and the river encircling it made this city a center of privilege and virtue.

Sacred Pyramid of
the Maya Sages.

The Power Animals and the Freedom.

The Cosmic Stone she had received, had again materialized with her will, but how did it happen she wondered? "Henceforth it will be my friend, companion and guide, especially because of the protection from this Messenger of the Mountains."

Yet, she also had to cleanse and transcend many of the actions and happenings in her past. For example, present in her genetic memory, recorded in her blood, was the death in her womb of one of her offspring in Egypt. An event that had manifested in her physical body through the swelling of her abdomen, as if she were pregnant. What she opted was to forgive in order to transcend. The way of the Sages of the Moon and the Sun, was her perfect guide.

Yet, her desire of communion and reverence was so considerable that one day, in one of her visions, **appeared the Spirit of the Mother Earth —a Lady dressed in a large white tunic, radiating a light of such brightness that it made it impossible to look at her. At the same time, from this light emanated a frequency of goodness and love never before experienced by Shazadi. As in a blessing, she felt this Great Lady placing a hand on her head and bestowing these words upon her:**

> **"There are persons who seem fond of bearing heavy loads! And life itself becomes a burden once accustomed to carrying them. There are also those who, as if their own encumbrances where not enough, choose to bear those of others so as to pass as victims, or to pretend to be the saviors of the world. It is important to understand that no one is anybody else's savior, and that a person finds the way only with their determined desire and will to change. If not, that person will live life out excusing, seeking forgiveness and appearing to be the image of a 'good person' in the eyes of others, although inside there is probably much suffering. The process of liberation and realization of the divine within each individual, requires a great responsibility. To recognize the capacity of expanding our own potentials is the key to progressing in spiritual discovery and development. In that way, once connected with the inner force, perceptions and decisions will become more complete and effortless, for we will know the most**

suitable moment for everything to happen. Life is full of decisions and there is nothing better than deciding conscientiously, in communication with the higher essence of the soul. Individuals are capable of going beyond their emotions, and discover that, with their inner strength, they can help to change the world for the better. And when you feel fulfilled and happy, in whatever place you may be, then you will be on the correct road. If not so, then you will have to search deeper in you heart for the necessary transformations to come about."

When she woke up from the dream of her latest voyage in timelessness, she searched for the stone in her vision and found it beneath her pillow. "How did this stone get here?" she asked herself. Yet she was so attuned to these most recent happenings, and the vision of her encounter with this timeless being was so vivid, that she decided to keep this crystal and call it a "Cosmic Stone."

When Shazadi felt restless, she preferred solitude. And in her meditations, the elements manifested themselves more vividly. She even felt the caress of the wind, the strength of the earth, the moisture of the surrounding environment attuned with her blood, and the warmth of things connecting with her soul, activating her inner Sun. These moments of internal peace were very necessary to her.

In one of her meditations, she felt the strong call of the mountains and, as if by magical design, the opportunity presented itself for her to travel to the Andes. A group of pilgrims from different parts in the world with whom she was keeping in touch, and also the group she was leading in meditations and releasing works suddenly organized the journey and the chance came knocking at her door. She had no option other than to comply with what her inner voice said, "Go and discover your essence in those lands of power in the mountains." The cards were laid out on the table and plain to see. Shazadi set off to revel in the land of Pachamama. A higher purpose had manifested itself and she was serving as an instrument for events unfolding in her own as well as other people's lives. When she made the decision to embark upon this pilgrimage, the Universe contributed to her effort and many doors opened to help her accomplish the trip, making everything flow easily and spontaneously.

From the moment that she accepted the call of the Andes, Shazadi began living within as many as three scenarios: Her contemporary life blended into her Egyptian life and then blended into her visionary life where she traveled through timelessness to the mysterious city of high mountains and beings living in harmony with nature, which they termed Pachamama. If she had so far never been able to identify this, the most mysterious of her lives, now was her opportunity to encounter, and address it, a remote and glorious past. The path of the Andes had, in other words, been laid out before her and she would now confront the reality of that Sacred Ground.

But in a similar but opposite way, the burdens and memories of the *akashic* world returned at times to her current life. One was the feeling of loss and despair she had felt by the banks of the Nile in a very distant time. This made her transport herself and attempt to grasp the meaning and understanding of what had taken place. Then, one day, in the midst of a deeply ecstatic experience, she was able to visualize that remote spot and moment and once again witness what had befallen the lovers—the conspiracy organized by Bernet, who was later to become her husband, to murder Amrep and her son. Everything became revealed, and she realized a connection relating to that happening with a series of simultaneous and interrelated events, where all and everything fitted into that place and event. After freeing herself from the past, Shazadi now had the opportunity to get to the bottom of things and, once and for all, to transcend the transitory and delve into the more sublime spaces of her own existence, which became manifest through love and forgiveness.

But life would open more doors in this new stage of her existence, and her desires to attain inner peace would be exposed during those moments of great connections. That which once had been only a vision, would now crystallize in her personal experience by coming face to face with the magic and the beauty of the land which the Andean Sages called Pachamama. The journey into the unknown, as well as magical and mysterious, was now a destiny decided and the Universe had created the conditions for her to turn this dream into reality.

JOURNEY TO THE ANDES

Many things in Shazadi's life remained unfinished when she decided to travel with the Pilgrims, more than twenty folks, all from different locations.

"I must take this journey before I can make any further decisions concerning my life," she told herself, feeling a certain security and inner peace, which she still did not understand. It was serenity, assured that all would fall into place along the way, and that her destiny would awaken her to her true path.

Her excitement at the thought of going to other lands with mysterious pasts and great histories, put her in meditative states and visions, as if all this were preparing her for something that perhaps she already knew of... On the night before the start of the trip, the Spirit of the Mountains again appeared to her:

Shazadi was in the Crystal City. Everyone was walking toward the Mountain of the Qori Q'ente (the Golden Hummingbird). The initiated in the Sacred Path were performing a Pilgrimage, and each new step was of great importance in their journey. The Master of the group told them, "Leave your minds free and your hearts open, let PACHAMAMA touch your hearts!" And in this way they pushed on until they reached the highest point on the mountain. From the summit, Shazadi could make out the Crystal City; it possessed a glow of its own and from these heights, the City had the appearance of a Kondor.

Shazadi felt... at the top of the World! "I am free," saying the words out loud, and then she bowed in reverence to the APUS, the Guardian Mountain Spirits. "When looking at these Mountains my problems seem so minute," she thought. Shazadi closed her eyes and connected with the Magic World around her. She floated, filled with energy and then, very slowly, started returning to the physical world.

The moment to begin the journey had come and so, off she went. Eventually, the travelers gathered in the airport at Lima, the capital of Peru, then went to a hotel. There Shazadi went to the first level of meditation to

The Spirit of Mother Earth.

Connection with Three Worlds.

Along the Path of Light toward the
Young Mountain of the Hummingbird.

invoke the protection of the Forces of Heaven and Earth throughout their journey. In the course of the ceremony, they could feel the energy of the Pacific Ocean, which lay close by, and its shores, in a different frequency, imparted their blessing upon the ceremony. Shazadi perceived what was in her outside and inside, for she was completely open and determined to see the positive aspects of this magical journey. She expressed gratitude for the granting of this opportunity. She was aware that she would have to unveil time and space in order to be fully present and cognizant in order to fully experience this mysterious and legendary world. To facilitate this, before the trip she had prepared herself and her group in a regimen of natural practices and philosophy that allowed them to be more aware of the subtle and insightful readings of themselves.

Shazadi felt that the energy of that place was not aligned with the emotions that she carried within herself. She then decided to create a separate space in her consciousness, reserved exclusively for the new events, an act that prepared her for entering the Magical lands of the Inkas. "I wish to find my true harmony in this life, and close my cycle. I wish to be reborn," she told the group, feeling animated. "I have discovered that, after experiencing pain, grief or fear, a person finds a space deep within, similar to entering an unfamiliar room in complete darkness, but as soon as it is lit, everything becomes clear. I find it very interesting to have found this magnificent space, laying underneath the pain that I was going through."

She pursued her reasoning further, "We are slaves to our thoughts, we are connected to those vibrations and it is in thinking that we draw to us all that we desire and need for our evolution, especially when we are attuned with our Divine essence. Our thoughts are a form of energy not to be wasted. This energy is sacred, as is everything that makes up our surrounding. It is important to observe everything and thus recognize the marvels of this world. And through a look, a gaze, a smile, appreciate a person's sincerity. Through thought we can create our own world," she continued sharing with the group.

Shazadi was conscious of everything that had touched her, since the day she decided to take this journey. Sensations, feelings, desires and emotions were blooming and bubbling up within her. "All my process has been accelerated inside of me," she thought very sure of herself. Shazadi could close her eyes and feel the energy of the mountains, the wind stroking her body and hair. She observed with detachment everything that lay around her. "I see that we are an outward reflection of that which lies within us, like signs of everything we have experienced. It is necessary to be aware and give attention to signs," she concluded to the group. Everybody entered in a space of peace and to be open to their experiences on this sacred journey.

In Lima they walked at the edge of the seashore. Along the way, they would come across different monuments erected in various parks and plazas overlooking the ocean. But there was one that caught her attention in particular, for it represented Love in the form of kissing couple. It was, in fact, named "The Kiss" and was surrounded by gardens, with a clear view of the Ocean.

Shazadi decided to concentrate on the present moment, on living the here and now. "I feel calm and serene, for I know that the transformations are forthcoming. Part of me already has transformed and I breathe with my heart, feeling its beats. I renew my entire self," and so thinking, assured herself once more that she was on the right path.

The next morning, one of her traveling companions approached Shazadi.

"We live as though we are contained in a box," he remarked to her.

"Yes!," she agreed, pensively, "but it is necessary to find a way out of that box and see that the Universe is far greater in order for our life to change," she assured him.

It was on a Sunday when, very early, they made the acquaintance of the spiritual guide who would be accompanying the group throughout the entire trip. This person was an expert on the Andean Culture, quite respected in Peru and in other countries. He was a spiritual leader of the Andes and initiated in the Shamanic path.

From the moment when they exchanged greetings, Shazadi felt a strong sensation of having already known him, feeling his strong magnetism and an undefined "something" that bound them. He apparently also felt that a superior force directed his energies in her direction. At times he followed her, unnoticed by others, but Shazadi was well aware of it, though she also knew that his purpose was only to work with her and her group in breaking their ties and attaining freedom in a deep way through a shamanic path. In those moments, she would ask in meditation to find a way to dispel her confusions.

"Hello, what is your name?" he asked her in friendly manner. It was early morning and they were in the hotel lobby.

"Shazadi, and yours?" She responded giving him a penetrating look.

"Puma Sinchi," he told her, returning the look yet in a way that seemed analytical.

During the next stage of the trip, Shazadi preferred to not pay any attention to him, or speak or look at him. His presence was very strong and could cause her to lose sight of the purpose of her inner quest. In addition, she thought, "Everything has its opportune moment and I feel that mine is now. My heart is confused and I need to calm myself and grasp the full understanding of my mission. I must get far away from all those have touched my heart and center myself. From there, I will know what direction to take in my life. I must dedicate these days to centering myself and afterwards, the answers which I seek so earnestly will come to me. But I know that this mysterious man is in some way linked with me, I can feel it. Sometime in the future, I will know the significance of all this."

It was not a tourist trip in which only moments of general historical and cultural interest were shared. Rather, this journey was a pilgrimage and meditations, energizing skills, breathing exercises and shamanic activities were regularly carried out. The experiences took place in accordance with the requirements of the group and the Center of Power being visited. "The Sites of Power of the Andes possess a very strong energy," Shazadi told herself.

They flew to Southern Peru to visit one of the largest and deepest river canyons in the world —the Colca. When they arrived at the area, they stayed in a hotel surrounded by high mountains that also had thermal springs. It was a place that vividly displayed the brilliant inspirations of nature. There were pools with water of varying temperatures, which were very relaxing.

Before traveling on to the canyon itself, they went to the town of Chivay. Along the way, they passed the highest point in the entire region with an altitude of 4,800 meters. This was a special place, where everyone of them gave an individual offering of stones, forming a pyramid in reverence to WIRAQOCHA - Great Spirit and PACHAMAMA - Mother Earth. Each one had to use seven pebbles: four in the base and three for the body of the pyramid.

Shazadi walked slowly about feeling the effects of the high altitude. Nevertheless, she felt very awake, filled with a great desire for Life. She felt a group of stones calling out to her and from among them picked her seven and proceeded to form her pyramid on top of a large rock that resembled a Kondor. Before that, however, she breathed on every stone and one by one placed them close to her heart, so that they would synchronize and attune with her heart *chakra*. Shazadi next connected with Freedom: "My desire is to be free," she told herself, while tightly holding her personal Cosmic Stone in one of her hands. After one last squeeze, she put it away in her bag.

Then, suddenly, she opened her arms and cried out her name to the Universe: SHAZADI! She then bowed in reverence to all the Beings of Light that inhabited the Area. Again thought about where her stones lay and visualized her pyramid expanding in all four directions. For Shazadi, every stone symbolized a part of her Life and it was of great importance to her to be completely devoted and attuned to the entire Divine Space. At the end of the ceremony all the group formed a circle of light holding hands in gratitude.

During the morning that they visited the canyon, nature offered them one of the most beautiful displays ever observed in their lives…the soaring of the Kondors. Words were insufficient to describe the surrounding landscape of high mountains and deep gorges plunging almost two thousand meters into the very bowels of the Earth. Because of the ideal atmospheric conditions and wind currents, the Kondors, the Great Lords of the Sky, delighted both themselves and those watching, in the magic of their flight.

The Kondor symbolized Strength and Freedom, for it flies higher than any other bird. A Kondor together with a Kolibri symbolize unity—the Kondor is strength and the Hummingbird is its essence. The entire spectacle provided a vision of nature worthy of noting in the histories of power and magic which any human being could hope to envision.

Shazadi got very emotional when she saw them and she floated in her thoughts. Already she was noticing that in each place that she passed, she released the energies that she didn't need and were not necessary in her life anymore.

The Andean environment and scenery in the dry season were almost desert-like but the magic expressed itself in the height and strength of the rugged mountains. The trip aboard the bus compelled Shazadi to put her hands to use, virtually to embrace this surrealistic landscape, touching them affectionately, feeling that she was making love with them in other dimensions. She was a daughter of these lands who was returning home after a period of time immemorial.

Following their encounter with the Kondors, they resumed their journey, heading for the city of Puno situated in the vast highland plateau known as the Altiplano, the region of Peru that includes the sacred Lake Titikaka. Regarded as the entry point or Pole of the Feminine Energy of the Planet, it is a deep and enormous lake, covering 8,500 square kilometers at an altitude of 3,810 meters above sea level. It contains many islands and small archipelagos. One of the most beautiful among them is Amantani, primarily because it is considered "the Island of Lovers" as well as for the existence of ancient temples over 4,150 meters high. The various communities that exist on the island continue to preserve the ancestral temples of their initiates. The island itself is situated on one of the virtual ley line routes that extend south from the Andes.

When they reached the island, night had already fallen and due to the darkness of the sky, far away from the intrusive presence of city lights, an infinity of stars shone, their clusters forming constellations in the shapes of mythical creatures. This island represented the ideal setting in which to learn about simplicity and open-hearted communion with nature through lodging in the homes of the native residents, a fantastic, albeit unpresuming experience. They were able to forget, or set aside, the confusing world of systems created by a society over-burdened with standards and codes, which each bearing its own label. Their sharing in the communal experience of the island's inhabitants, proved to be one of the ways they sought to confront their own "present times" and provided an opportunity to remember, return and relive their true essence and values.

At the same time, they gained a rich learning experience from a different and remarkable feature—the existence of a succession of seven portals, or initiatory gateways, from the lakefront to the center of the main village. The person who walks through them with humbly may even experience miracles. For that, it is necessary to be open and receptive to transformations. These seven portals, moreover, likewise lead to one's own inner path.

Let us review their represent:

+ The First Portal signifies Unity.
+ The Second, Polarity.
+ The Third, the Trinity.
+ The Fourth, the Four Directions and the Four Elements.
+ The Fifth, Equilibrium.
+ The Sixth, the Expansion into the Visible and Invisible.
+ The Seventh, the Holistic Being and its seven vital centers.

On the way to the Temples there are three more Portals:

+ The First symbolizes Tellurian Energy, represented by the SERPENT (Great Amaru). It activates the *Kundalini*—the creative energy and the sexual energy.
+ The Second relates to the SACRED PUMA. It embodies the force of self-control and inner balance.
+ The Third relates to the energy of the SACRED KONDOR. It stimulates the Self to look forward, to strive in the continual evolution.

As they proceeded onward, passing through every one of the Portals, they experienced the essence of these meanings. It was as if entering into the Magic World of the Andes, full of beauty and enchantment. Each Portal, also symbolizes the *chakras*, the centers of energy in the body which likewise are seven in number. Once entered into contact with the sacred ground of the Portals, a person feels the activation of their *chakras*. In the other three Portals the Presence of the Animal Creatures of Power are manifested, which provide assistance in the ascent of the Sacred Path for a person.

Throughout the course of this journey, each one was invited to ascend in silence and to get stones to make an offering in a special place. Shazadi focused all thought on her Life and she was aware of the presence of Beings of Light. Along the way she gathered stones that she felt called out to her, each one coming to represent an different area of her life. She passed through the First Portal, that of the Serpent, and headed for the ceremonial site of reverence and homage where the offerings of stones are deposited, the *apacheta*, located before the Second Portal. There, she built her pyramid of stones, but first she energized and programmed them with her intention: "These are for my professional life, the others for my health, love and family."

Before crossing the threshold a Center of Power, it is important and appropriate to give heartfelt honor, expressing gratitude and then requesting permission to enter into this Sacred Space. Respect is fundamental, for when one enters with humility and simplicity, in a state of communion with the Sacred Earth, transformations take place in the Self. For deaths and rebirths to happen, everything depends upon the level of receptivity and openness in each person. Sharing something with the Mother Earth is a way of being thankful for everything that has been received from her. This is why the Inkas, in their time, always performed their offerings. All over Peru there are places for the purpose of placing offerings of stones, *qoqa* leaves, flowers and others.

Shazadi felt her *Kundalini* energy activated when passing through the Second Portal and established a connecting force with this island of mysteries. After the Third Portal, she could already see above and beyond her emotions, feeling that her vision had expanded. "Truly, that person who is willing receives all the benefits of these Magical Lands. It is all so intense," she thought and continued her ascent toward the Temples, which make up important energy centers of the Planet.

Following along the path, to the left appears the Temple of PACHATATA. In the form of a rectangle, it symbolizes the masculine energy that fertilizes the earth. To reach this Temple, three more portals, symbolizing unity, must be crossed. Within it lies an open ceremonial space with stairways and a place for depositing offerings. There is also an Altar below surface level, representing the Feminine element balancing the Masculine as a sign of polarity.

Leaving the Temple, facing the opposite direction, there is a hill that leads to the SANCTUARY OF MOTHER EARTH. To ascend up to it, four more portals are crossed. These, added to the previously mentioned three, give a total of seven.

The Temple of PACHAMAMA or MOTHER EARTH has an octagonal ground plan, suggestive of a circle, which symbolizes the Feminine Element. Upon its altar rises a phallus, symbolizing the Masculine, balancing with the Feminine energy and achieving the Polarity already seen in the preceding temple. All around the inside the Altar has spiral constructions to serve as seats for participation in ceremonies and meditations.

Before entering this Sanctuary, one must walk around it in a clockwise motion to follow the biorhythm of the Planet and pay one's respects to the Feminine, inviting her to manifest her energy of vibrations of love and power in this Center of Light. It is the frequency of Pachamama that welcomes persons within her womb to show them the path of love and motherhood. To further experience this, women lie prone upon the ground, baring their abdomens of any clothing in order to keep it in direct contact with the bosom of the earth and thus feel its warmth and pulse, expressing Life and Freedom. This experience is an exercise in liberation that will activate vital centers, particularly those connected with creation and reproduction, especially that of the *Kundalini* energy manifesting as a serpent when stimulated. And by reason of it being the frequency of the Earth, who is our Mother, great emotions can be revealed including, at times, traumatic ones. Hence the purpose to be one of divesting the self of conflicts and traumas of a personal, social and family nature. It will be the earth, with her power, that will alchemize the life of the pilgrims. She invites them to breathe with her rhythm, allowing herself to be embraced in order to impregnate them with all her love, thus helping them to transcend and transmute everything that they no longer need to carry in their lives.

No matter how you look at it, this was a magical scenario, which beckoned Shazadi to express herself with the rhythms of the soul; she danced then and celebrated the moment. She remembered Egypt, where sacred dances were an expression of all times, that moved internal energies, especially those connected to each of the molecules with all the bodies, from the physical to those of greater subtlety and insight. A similar effect comes from the ascent of the pyramid with five levels that rise a few meters away from the Temple of

Pachamama. At this next site, Shazadi paid respect, placing her left hand to her solar plexus and the right hand upon her heart, as if drawing to her the energies of the Earth and the Sky respectively. In this way, she sealed and clinched a moment of glory, beauty and pleasure with the guardians of this Center of Power.

When night fell, they lit a bonfire some distance away from the house were they lodged. The group making a circle, Puma Sinchi performed a meditation with the pilgrims, intoning the mantra of the Sacred Fire (Willka Nina) after which they wrote on paper those things they no longer wanted to carry in their lives, threw them into the transmutable power of fire for it, in turn, to alchemize them, offering new opportunities. Shazadi, for her part, again connected with the Beings of Light who there present and also with the Sacred Fire, feeling at peace. In her paper she had written what she no longer wanted to bear: grief, pain and suffering from this and past lives. Then, concentrating, she placed it in the fire. She suddenly started weeping, feeling that her transformation, ripping and tearing through the fabric of time and space in a number of other levels, was coming about. The fire quickly died down and soon turned into a layer of glowing embers.

Puma Sinchi had prepared the fire at the same time that he intoned invocations to Willka Nina and uttered other native words invoking the presence of spirits. Now this fire had alchemized and turned to embers. To walk on glowing embers and coals is a shamanic technique acknowledging inner strength and courage and Puma Sinchi created in the pilgrims the energetic and emotional conditions for whomever felt the calling to walk upon these embers as a voluntary expression of freedom and power.

Shazadi walked them with tranquility and her feet were not burned. She concentrated, breathed deeply and connected with her Divine Essence, walking with her Soul. A feeling of strength accompanied her in those moments. After she was done, an energy of very strong heat flowed within her body, concentrated in the regions of her heart and solar plexus.

This experience represented an initiation at other levels for many, one that would remain in time until their own access to such levels of consciousness. Throughout the rest of the night, Shazadi retained the energy of the Sacred Fire and in her visions revealing cosmic connections.

On the following morning, Shazadi was serene. When she encountered Puma Sinchi, she clearly felt his energetic closeness, but chose to ignore it, for she was set on seeing through to conclusion her emotional and energizing processes that had originally brought her to these Lands of Power.

After some preparations, the group was set to depart the island and return to Puno. On the way to the docking area, they walked along the lakeshore and stopped at one of the beaches. There, they meditated, removed their clothing and waded into the crystalline waters of Lake Titikaka to cleanse themselves emotionally and physically. "What a magical moment this is," Shazadi told herself, "to go into these waters in the same way we came into this world." With arms spread wide, as if embracing its wholeness, she went into the lake feeling pure and free. Shazadi swam a bit and then let her body float in the water, letting the Sun energize every part of her skin and flesh. She felt that something invisible but representative of herself left her body and went into the waters.

They all felt like children in that translucent and almost immobile water where magic and purity were all that vibrated. Afterwards, they gathered on the sandy beach, forming a circle. In the center, they deposited the offerings each one had brought for PACHAMAMA, and they connected with the energy of the Sun. They then dug a hole in the sand and placed their offerings inside it and each of them communed with their personal individual feelings. They had also brought flowers, with which they formed into the outline of a heart. The flowers were of different colors, but many had shades reminiscent and representative of the hues of the Sacred Fire. Each of them knelt picked his flower, blew on the petals three times and after kissing it, completed the offering gently returning it the sacred geometric shape. The breath symbolized the soul and the flower a new life. Placing it in the center of the heart marked its connection with Universal Love, but, it was necessary to submit with one's own heart open to attain it, for gratitude was the key to communion with the beauty of Pachamama and the spirit of the lake, Mama Qocha.

In the evening, Shazadi kept her separate space and in the course of meditation, she found herself once more transported to the Crystal City, where the animal Creatures of Power again manifested:

In the Crystal City, Shazadi felt surrounded by Cosmic Serpents. They were all over her body moving up and down. She remained standing, with her arms open pointing in the four directions. She made her invocation to every Being of Light present at each point. In the North, she invoked the protection of the Golden Kolibri (Qori Q'ente); in the South, that of the Cosmic Llama (Katachillay); in the East, the Sacred Kondor (Kuntur Apuchin); and in the West, the Celestial Serpent (Hatun Amaru, the Cosmic Mayu, or River). Meanwhile, the serpents performed their work of energetic cleansing.

Shazadi, with this subtle insight, could contemplate the Magic World of the Crystal City, with its buildings of stone, agricultural terraces, temples, ceremonial plazas, and fountains, all laid out in accordance with the Cosmic Andean Feng Shui in the astronomic distribution of spaces, which would create an alchemical constant for the benefit of Pilgrims. For its builders knew the influence of the Cosmos upon the Self and their science made them a highly developed people, respectful of nature and who, by means of hard work, had found prosperity in a better world. The Masters and their disciples awaited the coming of the solstices and equinoxes to carry out work of inner development and spiritual growth. The SOLAR INITIATIONS were guided and aimed to seek the awakening of each Being, awaiting their respective moments to assist them in advancing along their own paths.

In every one of her timeless journeys, Shazadi felt stronger and more capable of undergoing anything necessary within and outside of herself. She grasped that the construction of this city was the result of the joint participation of a various sciences. This was clearly recognizable in its monoliths, thrones, altars and walls, all giving the city a very highly sophisticated degree of integration with its surroundings, without breaking the continuity of nature's own rhythm. As the Temple-City that it was, many spaces were dedicated and laid out for specific practices and activities. Shazadi discovered some of these to be familiar and she felt as if at home, blending within this soil.

They arrived in Puno aboard a boat from Amantani and headed north to Cusco. Along the way to the Imperial City, they stopped at "La Raya," an overlook point from where they could see the highest mountain in the area called Chimboya, whose melting snow feeds the first rivulets and affluent streams to form the Sacred River of the Inkas. This is also the site of an *apacheta*, or altar for offerings, and serves as the divider between the regions of Puno and Cusco. The landscapes are magnificent and magical, inviting them to be captured in film, drawing and painting, or in the memory of the soul.

The word "Cusco," or "Qosqo," signifies "the Navel of the Andean World." In olden times, the city possessed the shape of a Puma and during the June solstice there was a Solar Illumination of all its various spaces. This constituted a cosmic event of great importance and significance. The light first touched upon the head of the Puma, almost immediately afterwards the tail lit up and then the Sun gradually made its way up the backbone (Pumakurku) illuminating, as it went, the *chakras* of the Great Hatun Puma, starting with the sexual, to conclude at the crown.

In present times and during this period of the year, there are people who come seeking spiritual activities, either within Cusco itself or in the many Wakas, or Centers of Power, in the vicinity of the city.

On the day following their arrival, they proceeded to the Sacred Valley of the Inkas, a paradise area through which flows the Willkamayu, or Sacred River. This river, as previously noted, has sources in the glacial streams at La Raya and flows together in the vicinity of Cusco, thence to become one of two main tributaries of the great Amazon River which, after crossing almost the entire breadth of the South American continent, flows into the Atlantic Ocean at a point in present day Brazil. It acquires the name "Amazonas" upon reaching confluence with the Marañon River in northern Peru, entering Brazil joining up with the Solimões River. At this point its name changes into the latter (Solimões) until the confluence with the Rio Negro, flowing into it from the highlands of Guiana to the north, whence its name once again becomes and remains Amazonas until it flows into the Atlantic. Having altogether run a course no less than 6,400 kilometers in length, it is the greatest river in the planet.

A long way distant from most of that, back in the Sacred Valley, due to ideal conditions of climate, soil and altitude (average 2700 meters above sea level), one finds a wide range of crops—a great variety of fruits, legumes and grains, both exotic (imported) and native. Outstanding is a wide assortment of maize in virtually all colors, as well as the great size of kernels and ears. In current times there exist in this valley several contemporary towns (actually colonial villages or reservations founded by the Christians some 500 years ago) in which fairs and arts and crafts markets are held weekly. The native highlanders descend to the valley to barter and trade among the various communities for produce and craftsmen offer a rich variety of textile, ceramic and metal artwork. Many of these are reproductions of original objects found in Inka and older archeological remains.

Branching out from this valley, one can also visit other historical sites and, as a matter of course, access ancient Inka roads. One of these in particular attracting profound admiration among present-day pilgrims and visitors in general, is the so-called "Inka Trail," which leads to the Sacred City of Machu Picchu.

The group embarked on the adventurous journey along this hallowed and ritual road reaching the Sacred City. Their walk began at the point which, at present, is regarded as the "official" trailhead and is called "Piskakucho." There, the road from Cusco ends and a bridge spanning the Willkamayu carries travelers to the left bank of the Sacred River where the trail begins. Before crossing the bridge, in a ritual act consisting of joining three *qoqa* leaves—a *kintu* chosen for their beauty in shape, color and condition—they requested permission from Pachamama and the Guardians of the Pathway to allow them to enter and to assist them on their journey. Then midway across the bridge they paused and, after blowing three times on the *qoqa kintu*, they toss it allowing the Messenger of the Wind (Wayra) to carry away their offering and bless them. Then they began the hike.

This route is not only the once secret-sacred road that led to Machu Picchu, it is also a beautiful trail of history and magic. The group walked it in three and a half days and stopped at various Sites of Power along the way to review the time of glory and splendor of one of the most mysterious past civilizations known. Shazadi enjoyed every day of the pilgrimage, but this particular part of the journey gave her great satisfaction. The force and power of each day's scenery created dreams and visions that provided her with knowledge as well as answers regarding her own personal history. In one of them, she was transported for yet another visit to that place of fantasy, dream and magic, the Crystal City.

She was back in the Crystal City, it was still night time and Shazadi had been led to one of the Temples, where she came upon many people who sat in meditative position forming a circle. Over them, colors began to manifest, they were those of the Rainbow, and they blended forming new hues, creating an atmosphere of power and peace. These Beings of Light, along with the Animal Creatures of Power of the Andes, kept each other company within the vision. Shazadi knelt before an Altar, placing her hands in prayer. The Sun was dawning and its first rays touched Shazadi's Third Eye. This was one of the main rituals of the Inkas, which led them to Solar Initiation and was not privy to all persons. Those prepared were chosen and it was always a select group that participated in the secrets and magic of those lands.

And it was there that Shazadi first understood what was happening to her, for she needed to reconnect with parts of herself that had remained lost in time, in order to become a more complete being. The energy of her third eye expanded and her chakras began to activate one after another. Shazadi began to weep while receiving that energy of Love.

She then placed her left hand, bringing with it the energy of the Earth, upon her solar plexus (close to the navel, which functions as a center linked to emotions). Her right hand, bringing the energy of the Skies, she placed upon her heart. This is a posture of reverence in the Andean World and at the same time an embrace of the Self. It also represents the interaction of the Self with its Divine Essence and, by extension, the connection with the Universe. "It was an act of Love to my Person on the part of the Universe," she understood. "As of this moment I AM," and Shazadi felt fulfilled, understanding her deep interaction with nature.

Then, the Sacred Kondor appeared and carried her to the heights as a consummation of her transcendental experience. She perceived as of that moment, a new world opening to her. It was definitely a new beginning.

The Inka Trail goes through some very dynamic geography, with many steep ascents and descents. The Inkas had traced it among rugged mountains, following cobble stoned walkways, many stairways, passes and viaducts that spanned large precipices, tunnels, waterfalls and several ceremonial and historical building sites interspersed along the way. These ranged from lesser to greater with the last Inka centers (those closest to Machu Picchu) being larger and more elaborately built. The flora was varied, exotic and virtually all of it was originally native. There were few, if any, imported plants. All of this made for some of the most beautiful and contrasting scenery on earth.

Due to her good physical condition, the hike was quite easy, as if she were a daughter of these mountains. On the climb up to the main pass, she came across Puma Sinchi several times and, despite her determination to fulfill her process of cleansing and transformation, she could not avoid feeling the energies that surged from her Andean guide. With much respect and care, he diligently carried out his work as messenger and master with each one of the pilgrims. Puma Sinchi felt attracted by this stranger, yet also understood that she had to follow her own peregrination and visualize her mission on the Earth. With his experience and skill, he allowed himself to play subtle games with her, thinking that at some given moment things could be different and they would find themselves face to face without fleeing each other's presence. Nevertheless, this seemed not the place where Pachamama would confront them.

Along the way, each Pilgrim expressed themselves in their own manner. Some meditated and walked in silence; others sang, some conversed, but each of them attuned to their process of commitment, of forgiveness to themselves and others, of gratitude to life and of self encounter with themselves, with nature and with their inner divinity. Shazadi placed her feet firmly on the ground, allowing herself to ground her energies and follow the path of assurance and beauty.

It was recommended to leave the mind free, the heart open, and walk firmly, for greater results. When they came and entered upon sacred spaces, it was important for them to pay reverence with an open heart, radiating love. The bridge and connecting causeway for internal alchemy is the heart; concentrating on the breathing, paying attention to its rhythm, remaining open to transformations and remaining unattached to everything and everyone.

Each step on the Inka Trail symbolized an internal movement expressing itself externally. Shazadi was involved in a process of connection from before the journey, and once she placed her feet upon this land, she felt she was at home. This feeling kept growing. She was open and ready to leave behind all that she no longer wished to carry inside her, as PACHAMAMA had said in her apparition.

Shazadi had the opportunity to discern what she wanted to change and the willingness to expand herself was so great that she sometimes ran along the trail. She took her steps with joyfulness, peace, love and the desire of dancing. Shazadi understood that, because of this experience, she would be capable of feeling at ease within everyday life. She clearly understood what took place around her was first born within her. "The initial motion always stems from within us, like the waters that spring from the mountains and find the space for the growth of their flow while flowing gently," she thought. "Yes, one step at a time. Through each step we feel stronger and build a foundation of life with well-grounded energies," she concluded, sure of her rationale.

On the second night, Shazadi went to bed early and took advantage of the extra time to pray and meditate. At that moment she went into trance and came upon another Center of Power:

Initiation and
Reverence.

Rapanui - The Island of the Moais.

Activation of the Inner Fire.

RAPANUI, ISLAND OF THE MOAIS – EASTER ISLAND

Shazadi had incarnated once in Rapanui, Easter Island, which was settled by peoples of wisdom in pre-Inka times. And, though its surface was small, the landscape was like paradise. At the time she lived there, the communal chiefs were building more structures for their people. They erected stone monuments with human faces that served as instruments for ancestral memories as well as concentration of tellurian forces.

Shazadi had been born here in order to learn various techniques of healing therapy for men and women, as taught by the medicine of this ancient land. For this island, lost in the ocean, was a retirement center for the Sages of the Sea, who read the secrets of the waters and the winds, and it was a place of importance to them where they could learn about detachment and cosmic connections. In this Center of Power, Shazadi was to learn about liberation and alchemy at levels she would not be able to attain anywhere else.

In those times, initiates from different parts of the world came to the island, following the call to do so at some point in their lives from their inner Self. Then in order to reach this destination, they would surrender themselves to the greatness of the ocean, going far beyond the regular limits of their own lifetimes. Some of them later returned to their lands of origin, while others remained here to educate the visitors and pilgrims.

Shazadi, in her native island, would undergo some of her greatest confrontations with her own essence and with the spirit of nature. These experiences would later help her to live with the Maya people and in her continuous inner voyages, also the high mountains of the Andes. She first had to ground herself in the elements of nature, to later count with them as allies in the fulfillment of the great secrets of her own timeless reality. This island would teach her how to penetrate the secrets of her own soul, understanding that for love to be as such, would have to surge and be born in her limitless inner dimensions, radiated by her physical heart.

Otherwise, had she not taken this momentous step, she would never have had a lover or mysterious beings in her life. And the experiences, at the physical and emotional level, obtained in this small paradise, would not have contributed to the freedom that her soul sought. She now remembered that time is the best teacher for transcendence, and that we only succeed in entering upon the path of liberation when we are prepared and willing to open the heart and free the mind.

Already in her adulthood, Shazadi formed a union with a pilgrim and, in communion with him, enjoyed the gifts that the Universe had to offer them. She learned that the act of loving with her physical nature opened the doors to touching her soul. She knew that if something is undertaken, one should be able to live it through, for the sum of all experiences would transform her into the woman of wisdom, which inside her she already was. Life was teaching that her greatest purpose ought to be the satisfaction of obtaining the necessary balance and equilibrium of all her bodies. Something that would express itself through a stable mind and body that would enable the windows of her soul to light each morning, and her light transforming the darkness of her inner world.

Various lives serve the purpose of our personal growth, not unlike the barriers that are necessary to surmount any learning process. We must be alert in order to prevail over them. To acknowledge our possibilities us wiser and overcoming them gives us freedom. Being free, we obtain the longed for peace.

From this island of isolation and universal connection, Shazadi was able to transport herself to other spaces and times, especially to the Crystal City, a city of mysteries and magic riveted in the midst of the mountains. In spite of being physically unknown to her, it always seemed familiar as a city symbolizing love, tenderness, strength, pleasure and beauty. She felt that someday she would find it. She was certain, however, that it existed inside of her and nostalgia made her travel to the horizons of that bottomless blue sea. Yet the Sun of every new day came to illuminate her body and her mind, and to guide her soul. Then, feeling satisfied, she went into a deep sleep.

At dawn of the third day of hiking on the Inka trail, Shazadi woke feeling both relaxed and excited by the revelations of the previous night. She then took advantage of an opportunity offered by one of the attractive cascading waterfalls in the vicinity by taking a bath and experience the element of water. Acknowledging its virtues, she invoked the Guardian Spirit to manifest cleansing and refresh her physical body, also enabling her mind to open so that her soul would receive the blessing of the sky.

That evening after setting up camp Shazadi did her daily meditation and the visions manifested most convincingly:

She saw herself after the pilgrimage returning to her present native land, Mexico, and when searching for the places where she lived and worked, finding nothing. There was only emptiness. This vision left her very pensive, but she could still not make out what it meant.

"It is interesting to note that on the Inka trail and in the Centers of Power, the channels of perception and sensitivity become intensified," she reflected immediately after waking up.

On the fourth day of the hike, they were led to the ceremonial fountains of one of these Inka Centers and, after paying reverence to the water, allowed themselves to continue walking until reaching Wiñay Wayna, which symbolically means "Eternally Young." Here, they performed their last ceremonial ritual and set off on the final stretch of trail to reach the Sacred City of Machu Picchu. They reached its Gateway only in the afternoon and their first act was to express their thankfulness for all the beautiful experiences that these mountains had given them, their weariness polarized by the energy of the place. The Magic City rising before them, appeared as a virtual projection of beauty and precision, and everyone felt the inner calling to pay their reverence to it and its energetic guardians. Nature's whimsical genius expressed itself through the presence of a rainbow, paying respects to the name CITY OF THE RAINBOW, given to it once by an initiate.

Puma Sinchi saluted the City and explained to the pilgrims its significance. He told them that, by virtue of its luminous characteristics and tellurian energies that expand to the skies, as well as the high content of granite and quartz, he himself had given it the name of **CRYSTAL CITY**. When Shazadi heard these words, she felt that her soul recognized this site of fantasy and dreams and could hardly believe what she heard.

In the course of so many visions she had visited this city, always encountering the Mysterious Messenger, and now she was hearing from the mouth of her guide and fellow companion admitting that he himself had given it that very name. It couldn't be, it seemed impossible... yet he undoubtedly revealed himself as the mysterious creature who always appeared to her in other times and lands and who had been waiting until today to share with her so many common spaces. Shazadi's heart vibrated and tears ran down her blushed cheeks, but they were tears of happiness and realization at having found the magic place she had always sought. Opening her arms, she thanked heaven and earth but uttered not a word, preferring to rely on silence to meditate in peace on everything that had happened throughout the pilgrimage.

When the Sun had set, the moment came for them to physically leave the Sacred City. They descended the mountain to the town of Aguas Calientes, named because of the thermal hot springs that exist there. They unpacked and prepared to take a ritual bath in the liquid fire that emanated from the earth at this site. They had a pool privately reserved for them. There in small ceramic receptacles oriented in the four directions, they lit four flames representing the incandescent element of fire which, in addition to the liquid fire represented by the hot spring, would rise to the sky and assist to alchemize the life of these pilgrims who had been chosen with the grand purpose of reconnecting with this sacred land. Once the ritual bath was finished, they found that it had given satisfaction to their physical body but also activated the inner fire of each so that like the Crystal City, their own personal crystal, or luminous force, would reveal itself to transmute time and space.

On the following day, they again visited the CRYSTAL CITY, and each one meditated and offered their personal offerings. Shazadi found herself open and aware, in a renewed state: "I feel that I have left behind those needs which I thought were important to my life," she thought. "While I bathed, I knew that everything had changed in me and that things had a different meaning now. I forgave those who had done me wrong and I forgave myself. I freed myself from the feelings of other lives. Once cleansed, I closed the past cycles, opening a new way for myself."

Shazadi was very perceptive: "In the passing of our lives, we accumulate many things that are really of no use to us, just like unenlightened people for example who lead a listless and basic life whether they are rich or poor. For physical richness, is a material energy that generates other material energies. Within the circle of that type of life (the box as I used to think) we only survive. But to truly live, the expansion of the soul is necessary. We are all able to do it but it is necessary to prepare oneself, take care and learn to enter into the one's heart without the control of the mind," was her final conclusion.

Standing with her feet parallel and facing it, she meditated with the sun. Her body faced the mountains. She then opened her arms and with her hands in praying position, elevated them slowly while intoning invocations in each of her *chakras*, from the base to the crown. She ended with honoring the Father Star.

Shazadi was living a dream come true, ecstatic at being there. She had visualized the Crystal City during so many lives and now she was really there. Each part of the city, every building and detail, it was all as in her visions. She was determined to delight in every moment: meditating, singing or just simply admiring so much beauty. "At this moment I can say that nothing is impossible," she smiled, sure of herself. The feeling she had was that everything would assume a new meaning; every vision, every sensation, every message, all were connected. From Egypt to the present times, she understood that from the very beginning she had been led and guided on her way.

"I am a Universal Pilgrim," she thought, while she held tightly her Cosmic Stone, which continued traveling with her through time and space and sometimes laid itself out as a sort of bridge for her to cross. "It is incredible how everything that we need, at some given moment reaches our hands and just when it is needed. I know that it depends on an internal receptivity and openness for this to occur, yet absolutely everything has a reason. Every moment I have passed through and the decisions I took were indispensable for me being here right now," she acknowledged, contemplating the Rainbow that had once more appeared in the sky. "It represents the transmutation, the inner journey, it is the Portal of Transformation," she thought, integrating its significance and feeling ONE with the magical world opening for her with all its colors.

Upon completing these transcendental and eventful days, they all returned to the Puma City of Cusco. That night, they gathered for dinner and spoke about their experiences during the trip with each other. Shazadi shared her visions and expressed her thankfulness for the opportunity of being there with them. The celebration was enhanced by dance and song and she knew that it was a time of decisions, for it was the last night in Cusco; the next morning she would fly to Lima and that same day catch a plane back to her country.

Events during the pilgrimage unfolded in the manner that the Universe had planned them to, and the meeting of two souls was about to happen, albeit they did not know that they were already connected. Although the trip was finishing, new doors were opening for everyone including Shazadi. It was her last opportunity to settle experiences and transcend other dimensions involving her heart. For that reason, the Universe provided new circumstances for her and Puma Sinchi to finally encounter each other. This had to happen within the short period of time that was remaining. She had accepted his invitation to come to his apartment in order to speak more freely, but time was running so short that perhaps it would all end in only a friendly moment. Shazadi had clearly accepted her progress and felt directed to motivate Puma Sinchi and ask him to put aside all metaphors and tell her precisely what he had to tell her, for she felt that whatever had to happen would happen in the short period of remaining time.

"Yes," he responded, and remained silent for some moments, after which he continued, "I would have liked to have had more time to get to know you, but this was not possible, because you were carrying out your spiritual activities and following your own path. This did not give me the opportunity to approach you as I would have wanted to."

Glancing at her wristwatch she confessed, "During these fifteen days I completed cycles and experienced deaths and rebirths. I had many interesting visions that led me to understand the process of my life. I felt you seeking me out from the first day, but I chose to devote all this time to pursuing my goal. I think that perhaps we have known each other in past lives and I do not know the true purpose of our meeting again. But what I am sure of is that I want very much to be close to you.

"We have to pick up the group up in twenty minutes and transfer everything to the airport," he said, confessing the urgency of things. "But I want you to know that what I am searching for in my life is someone to grow together with and share this world of magic and power. The time being rather short at present to express to you my desires and visions, I want to invite you to return here after you finish your activities in Lima with the group. If your answer is 'yes' I will take care of everything and see to it that your stay here will be safe and comfortable," said Puma Sinchi.

"Give me twenty minutes to think about it and I'll give you my answer," she responded, as they quickly left for the hotel where the group was staying. Shazadi had given herself twenty minutes to decide, enough time for her luggage to not be checked and bound for Mexico.

"Good Morning," said Puma Sinchi, greeting the group, "everyone ready? The bus is here and waiting."

The group started to board the bus and Shazadi only then had managed to get her things ready, packing them haphazardly and managing to close her two suitcases. Once at the airport they stood in line at the ticket counter. Shazadi stood there with them. Puma Sinchi searched her face for signs of an answer if she would return to Cusco or go on back to Mexico. She was gripping her Cosmic Stone very tightly and meditating. During the activation of her third eye she visualized two doorways—one was Mexico and the other, the Andes. If she opened one of them, the other would automatically close, with no option to change her mind.

"I know that there are two options and I must choose only one. I must listen to my heart," she thought. Shazadi heard the cries of her family calling her and, at the same time, remembered her visions of Machu Picchu. And she decided to listen to her heart. She had to quiet down her thoughts, rid her doubts and enter her heart.

"Yes! The answer is yes, I shall return," she decided, giving him an affirmative sign. Puma Sinchi immediately separated her luggage from that of the rest of the group. And in this way it was once and for all decided. Shazadi went with them to Lima, individually bid them good-bye, rested and the next morning returned to Cusco to meet with Puma Sinchi who was waiting for her at the airport. They spent days together and for the first time gave each other the opportunity of sharing not only their thoughts but their bodies and souls as well.

A few days after their final coming together, other pilgrims arrived and also walked the Inka Trail. Shazadi joined the group, already with a different vision and experience, participating in the guiding, since she already knew the way. During the trip, Puma Sinchi and her had much to talk about. They both became close and assisted each other at every moment. Shazadi, however, still took the time necessary to pursue her meditation since each step of the pilgrimage was of importance to her further ground her energies that had been opened. Along the Inka Trail, she found a special place to return her Cosmic Stone as an offering to PACHAMAMA, for she felt that the moment had come to separate herself from it, having finally acknowledged that the magic and power were within her. The way to thank PACHAMAMA for her company throughout the entire process was to bury the stone in the earth, while she prayed to her. Finally, she knelt and kissed the Earth in an act of respect and love.

She now felt stronger, her emotions and feelings had calmed as she closed a cycle, feeling cleansed and free. She shared the next fifteen days with Puma Sinchi, thus setting the foundation to recognize who they really were and what they wanted. However, she would additionally have to make other great decisions in her life.

Andean Kondor

TITIKAKA

Once again they journeyed together to the Sacred Lake Titikaka. There they visited one of the most fascinating Centers of Power in the area, situated atop the outcropping of Kesanani where a pre-Inka astronomy observatory exists. That morning, Shazadi found a spot to sit and meditate; she closed her eyes and came into contact with the Magical World that still existed there.

She had a sensation that she was floating. She approached the two columns that support a ceremonial altar where the Sunlight touches it on solstice days. Puma Sinchi was waiting for her and he asked her to embrace one of the stone pillars. Within a few minutes, a ray of Sunlight hit her forehead, it was her Solar Initiation of the December Solstice at this Center of Power. Her inner vision began opening and unveiling more profound mysteries about herself, initiating a new path of enlightenment or spiritual ascension.

The Andes had offered her a stronger perspective of life and she felt grateful for all the new opportunities to continue growing. She felt ready to continue learning and to share the wisdom of ancient times with this generation.

Shazadi was ecstatic with this solar initiation and inspired with the voices of her divine self, thought about the keys that humans had forgotten use to open new doors in their own lives. The sensation of being at this magical site was transcendental to her and provided a greater source of inspiration.

"We are conditioned by and because of everything that we see, and the material things seem like priorities in this material world, without any regard for our feelings. We follow creeds and seek religions to find a greater meaning to our existence: we pray, beseech and gratefully thank. We beg God to fill the emptiness of our lives, we clamor in desperation for HIS salvation, flock to temples and ask guidance and advice from priests, monks, ministers and pastors. They reward us with words of consolation, which help in some way. Significant help, undoubtedly, but change must begin and stem from within our own self."

"The higher meaning of Life lies in each one of us. And I imagine a better world, without religions, for religion creates rules and regulations in order to subject the individual to its control and provokes fears and worries when the individual does not correspond to the principles of those gods imposed by religions. People are always motivated and encouraged to seek in religion, what they already possesses within themselves. Thus they are taught to fear God. It is an altogether different matter when an individual pursues an inner path and from there decides to become a follower of a particular sect or religion to live."

"We use convenient clothing and then store them away in the dresser, waiting for the fashions to return. We concern ourselves about tomorrow and what our future will be and conditionally project our happiness on a given event or a distant place. 'When I marry someone, only then will I be happy, because I alone cannot be.' 'When I move to a foreign land I shall achieve a better life.' And so we go on, escaping from ourselves."

"We cling to our memories and recollections, remaining prisoners to the past.... of relationships that were not successful, projects that never succeeded, the death of a beloved one. There were and still are individuals who became ill and died after the death of loved one. We attach ourselves and cling to people, things and situations in order to feel more secure. It is as though most times we need to have control of everything in our own hands—control of time, and of the emotions."

"We exist ignoring the fact that everything can unfold in a different manner. That happens when the person begins to question theories and rituals and realizes that one can pray anywhere he or she can attain Oneness with God, who is the Ruling Force of the Universe. In any case, the ultimate importance being that *the individual retain his/her link to the divine while he or she look deeper within their inner being.* That creates an authentic labor of renewal, since truth from their inner state, open to connect with their divine essence."

"From then on the person establishes a flow, constantly connecting with their inner self. Otherwise, they remain limited, self-conditioned, punishing themselves as well as others with their inner reality waiting, immersed in pain and suffering, bearing hidden truths in the likeness of treasures lost. Realities are replete with repressed illusions, desires and emotions and with lives filled with fantasies and frustrations, simply surviving." Shazadi spoke this with assuredness, knowledge of a human reality, of those who possess but a basic life and seek not a superior way or one through which to find the inner self."

Shazadi wanted to continue speaking, she was enthralled by spiritual themes and felt increasingly inspired through being at a Site of Power in front of the Sacred Lake Titikaka. So she went on:

"We constantly crave more than what we need, we are never satisfied. Yet, what about time? We never have time for anything, we are always occupied and in a hurry, time is always encroaching, threateningly, so we fill it and occupy it or distract it in order to feel useful and thus forget what is truly important to us. We remember what is of importance to do, yet neglect a brief pause to reflect upon what lies around us and forms part of our lives. And what of our lives? They are all the same, some with greater and other with lesser material goods. And when we do reflect upon it all, we perceive that time passes quickly, as do we, and those we love. We have no control over anything and what we live is but an illusion, for all we take from this life is whatever we manage to BE in our day-to-day existence. *The more we are, the more we have to Give, the more we Give, the more we RECEIVE.*"

"Love is the greatest of virtues, and when we realize the Great Love we have within us, our life expands and makes more sense to us. It is necessary to experience that Love in all its abundance, granting us all the joy and happiness that lies within our reach. Silently gazing within ourselves, we feel our potential. Hence, it is necessary that, each day, we BECOME OUR DIVINE ESSENCE, and bring into action all that we are. "Our perception of ourselves needs to be expanded and in that way we become further acquainted with ourselves, our awareness of others becomes enhanced and thus we gain entrance to our souls. It is possible for each one to enter this inner, intimate place, visualizing how special and unique we are. The Life we have received is sacred and it is up to us to live it well, enjoying every moment and realizing the beauty of life itself. Everything should be beautiful, as we are two in one having both sides, the polarity and its options in every moment."

"If we remain alive, our heart shall be wherever Love lies and all fear will vanish."

"Our past needs to be understood, where we come from, what we feel, what our reactions were before the steps that allowed us to become who we are. We possess a history, written by ourselves, one where we are the both the characters and the authors, and it is duly registered. We know that each of us is made up of many parts—a thousand, a million, an infinite number of them—where we store memories of reactions, sensations, feelings, and emotions. Due to this, we are capable of repeating behaviors. I have observed that within a family behavior is repeated. Because these records exist, they add the memory that is impregnated in each cell of our body. Each being has his or her own internal baggage of rich experiences. There are persons who are capable of seeing their past lives, and there are others who cannot. But what is most important is to identify what registers each day and transcend them."

"And so, when undertaking the process of cleansing, we always receive the tools necessary for our growth. Those who have visions of their past lives and communicate with the Beings of Light, need these tools to free themselves. When a person is open, the Universe places an opportunity in their hands that is needed for their evolution. This process of cleansing is necessary at all levels, physical, mental and spiritual. In the **physical** level, it is accomplished through daily activities. At the **mental** level, by means of creativity, good habits, breathing exercises and discipline. At the **spiritual** level, through the practice of meditations, fasting, spiritual cleansing, invocations, good thoughts and good actions."

"As we increasingly understand our emotions, feelings and reactions, we can go beyond the limits and confront every aspect of our lives. Thus we will recover every part of us that we have lost. I envision the human being as a Whole, and there are parts of us that in some other life remained caught, imprisoned, abandoned, or lost. Then the moment arrives to rescue all of these parts and we feel that we are becoming more complete. When we have a vision or strong emotions that block us in this life, that is the moment to transmute or transform ourselves."

"In order to do this, one way is to visualize the violet flame which enters through our head and fills our entire body. We then ask for protection to the Beings of Light, who are the angels who accompany us in our growth. Invoking the violet ray, we create a frequency for our *inner alchemy*. Another technique is to visualize the Sacred Fire in our forehead and while keeping our eyes closed, we place our emotions in a bundle or sphere and cast it toward the Sacred Fire with our breath. Immediately following this, the golden, blue, and pink lights emerge from the Fire and fill the empty space, bringing us a sense of peace and harmony. We can do this with all our emotions and feelings."

Shazadi felt the need to continue speaking. There were many invisible beings around her and in that moment, time and space seemed split apart. The Magical World of the Andes lay open before her. She experienced a parallel world that comprised all that she believed in. It was the world of magic and light.

"Could it possibly be that we are mere particles that united form the matter into our organs?" She asked herself, "What is our Human side? The words 'IS' or 'BE' already indicate existence. We exist! Is it not magnificent? Within the very expression 'HUMAN BEING' we can ascertain that 'the body possesses something more.' It means that we are a complete, therefore capable of loving, dreaming, feeling, living, desiring, evolving. We are part of a same Universe, a product of this Universe. I compare this Universe to the ocean and each person to a river, who sets forth on a course that will end in the ocean."

"The entire Universe is one, we were created with the same energy and form part of a constant flow, which is life. Everyone takes along with them their knowledge and expertise from all the time they have spent on this Earth. We are all interconnected, like in divine essence. We have a same origin, and what is interesting is that we all flow together into the same vast Ocean of Light. Some part of us dies, but it is reborn new and improved. This process takes place at every moment and we are in a state of constant mutation. I have listened to many people speaking of spirituality, of their own search and I have reflected a lot on that respect. I believe that the human being already is spiritual in his real nature: *we are spirituality in a potential that needs to be recognized, discovered, touched by our own selves. All the answers we need or seek are already within us,"* she asserted with conviction.

"It is necessary to placate the mind and tune into our divine essence, through meditations we connect and allow the thoughts to flow. It is important to leave the mind free and the heart open, to flow like the waters of a river. With our eyes closed we aid ourselves to disconnect from the outer world and so become calmer, following our intuition to a greater awareness."

"When I refer to the heart, I do not mean the organ that beats close to the surface of our body, but to the place that dwells within the depths of noble sentiments. In that place the self connects with its own wisdom and the illusory life becomes transformed into a superior reality. It is a new life, that validates one's self, as the great potential, as the infinite wisdom. And, if many times we cannot see what lies inside us, we can never the less feel it. For that, it is important to be infused with the conviction, *I believe in my potential and I fulfill it."*

"What is Life? I always asked myself what the real meaning of that word could be. Some ask, 'How are you? How is your life?' And we respond, 'I'm doing well, thank you.' In the society we live in, one lives distant from the heart–and I am not referring to one's companion but rather of one's own heart. One should breathe with the heart, with the soul and not merely with the body and mind."

"In our lives, we accumulate many emotional debris, traumas, insecurities, fears.... and we resort to the mind to rationalize it all. We gather so many negative emotions from this and other lives and so encounter difficulties and hardships to live an authentic life. An individual, who is authentic, knows it is necessary to assume responsibility for whomever one is, assuming the Being in the fullness of its abundance and with that obtain freedom. Once you assume who you are, you become a free person, with visions of life quite different than ordinary people."

"This is because we go about creating restraints everywhere; energetic fetters that imprison us, causing depression and dissatisfaction within a daily routine. In this way, persons become increasingly more dependent on one another, in a noxious and harmful way, and burden themselves with obsessions to fill their emptiness. This keeps recycling and is very difficult to overcome. They have no incentive to pursue their lives and stop caring for themselves. Because they no longer love one another and faced with so much disenchantment, they end up lost, only surviving rather than living, filled with insecurities and fears. It snowballs inside a person until they become ill and the negative emotions become imprisoned in their body."

"Illnesses begin that way, many of them created by our thoughts. It is our thoughts that become words and then create actions that later make the difference in the day-to-day existence and cause life to be very superficial, full of illusions. Each day, happiness that is sought from material things, in the act of HAVING, makes it worse. That is how I see the world, with humanity programmed and repetitive, where even expressing one self is difficult. This is all the more so for males because they've been taught that 'men don't weep,' and therefore a sign of weakness, thus denying the expression of their feelings."

"In many of people's histories, the guilty party is always someone else, 'it is her fault or his fault, that I am in this state,' 'the fault is theirs, not mine.' Individuals seek to justify their actions through other persons, precisely because they do not want to confront their own lives. It requires almost too much courage to stop excusing or justifying oneself because of other people. This is how they begin leaving behind their dreams and their fulfillment."

"Thus, it was interesting that I should inquire about the meaning of the word 'LIFE,' for the majority of humankind leads an insignificant life, very small, and they do not care because it weighs more than they are able to bear. Difficulties and setbacks are the most common features and people feel that it is impossible for them to do what they want, that time does not allow for their fulfillment, and as time passes the true concept of life for them vanishes with it and they live with illusions. Then with the passing of the years, they die without knowing that their life could have been different, that life could have had more."

"The individual always justifies itself and does not strive internally, refusing to look within the own self, more dedicated to observing the faults of others. 'I lost such and such an opportunity because of him, or her, or them.' 'I cannot educate myself because I have a husband and children,' 'I did not marry because I had to take care of my family.' There are so many people who are dissatisfied with their lives who have allowed this to happen even though they live in a manner seemingly easy and comfortable yet lack any inner pursuit."

"Then there is the moment when life becomes altogether too unbearable to them and it seems too difficult for them to continue. Then, because the word LIFE possesses a superior purpose, precisely due to its DIVINE nature, they see the reality of things and choose to assume responsibility for their own lives."

"The task of personal and inner improvement demands courage, detachment and unselfishness, patience, willpower, forgiveness and love:

- **Courage** to confront oneself, to recognize and admit one's emotions and feelings, of knowing one's body and to open oneself to transformations, to the inner alchemy.

- **Detachment** to understand that we are passing through this Life. To know that we lose nothing or anyone, for we possess nothing or anyone, everything having been granted to us by the Universe as instruments and tools for self improvement and we continue sharing what we are, giving and receiving. From this life we take with us only that experience and knowledge which we succeed in awakening within our own selves. Our body and all or any material possessions that we may have accrued remain here. If one knows that death is but a transit to other dimensions, according to the level of enlightenment reached, and a process that allows us to change "attire" with a different body in each of our lives. If one knows this, it is not difficult for a person to become detached at all levels. When an Awakening of Conscience is attained, the Self manages to see things with greater clarity and with daily training and discipline to Awakening of Conscience is attained, the Self manages to see things with greater clarity and with daily training and discipline to become present in body and soul. Once this level is achieved, one lives the present, free of past and future, shedding all of these projections. Enabling the detachment of the self, benefits each moment of Life, giving the best of itself.

- **Patience** to await the opportunity for the precise moment of each inner movement in accordance with the process that is being lived, knowing to do so with calm and grace in order that life may flow naturally.

- **Willpower** is the determination to break away from the cycle of an illusory artificial life. This desire provides the attainment.

- **Forgiveness** of one's self and those persons who they have lived with. This word is endowed with high vibrations and is of great aid in breaking energetic barriers and burdens. When we wish to release our emotional loads, the act of Forgiveness is of extreme importance in the cleansing of negative emotions, which the individual may carry for years. It must be understood that we are all interconnected and linked, hence, as the Masters have said, "forgive that you may be forgiven." By reason of this complete and mutual connection, each of our acts of forgiveness causes an effect felt throughout the entire Cosmos. When we forgive we create a more enlightened and homogeneous environment for the circulation of the energy of growth and expansion of the Being. Through forgiveness it is important to allow one's self a new life.

- **Love** by virtue of being the language of Gods and Goddesses, without it life would not exist. Love is the purest form of energy remaining in the world, as well as the one that transforms those energies of heavier density. The human being, when leading a basic common life, dwells far from the heart. But when we open ourselves to a path of inner awakening, we soon begin to gain access to our heart and the gift of breathing within it. This is a Divine action that will continue growing within us until reaching the moment when we are capable of transforming our life and LIVING MORE PROFOUNDLY. At that point we live with our own soul and come to create our Life with even more LIFE. These persons are joyful and open to spiritual growth, who assume and set forth upon a PROJECT OF LIVING SOUL."

"These are the steps and stages of *inner alchemy*, to become extricated from the cycle of previous life; thus we have a simultaneous birth and rebirth. But it is of the essence to undertake it without expectations, only being open and filled with the intention of a New Life. In time we understand that this motion of death and rebirth is constant, as long as we continue on the Spiritual Path. It is as a result of this that we may, many times encountering people and situations that we recognize and places where we have been, realize that we have already lived this life. It is then that we realize our path lies somewhere else, beginning a new life in which everything is different, although one has self confidence and freedom, of desire and of love," she concluded her explanations.

Shazadi felt renewed and decided to return to Mexico to take care of pending matters and say goodbye to her relatives. She was at the same conscious of all the confrontations that she would have to overcome in order to organize her new life. But this land had given her so much that she felt the urge to share her visions with Puma Sinchi and so she wrote him:

LOVE IN EMBERS

Dusk has come… night delicious as never any other.
I awaken from a long deep sleep.
Lips touching, a green light for the Love.
For a moment, colors blend,
green becomes transparent,
amidst hungry looks.
What could it be?
A beginning that already seems to bear meaning
passes through our minds in convulsion.
The embrace brings security.
The kiss drowsily lingers. Magic sensation.
Becomes a hypnotizing wave.
Wave… that liberates.
The freedom of being, and always loving.
Loving much and every time more.
Loving you.
I + You = LOVE
Love in flames. You call to me.
Love in Embers.

We shall soon be together again. I will conclude my life in Mexico but I will need some time to wrap everything up in my own way. I wish to give back to the Universe what I received with much Love. I must finish this to start a new life by your side.

With Love,

Shazadi

RETURN TO MEXICO

Feeling nostalgic yet determined, Shazadi returned to Mexico. The family chauffeur was waiting for her at the airport. As a sign of gratitude she gave him a handcrafted Andean gift.

Shazadi was all too conscious of the work she would have to go through in order to bring to closure what she had accomplished in her country, all the more so in the case of her business enterprise now in its tenth year. During her trip back she let her thoughts run free and paid attention only to the visions she'd had in the Andes.

The family awaited her coming in a festive mood, and her return was cause for much celebrations. Shazadi told them of the events she had participated in during the month she spent in Peru and they listened attentively but did not seem willing to place much belief in her visions and decisions. They were concerned she might wish to return to live in Peru, too far away from them! Shazadi was very happy, the sparkle in her eyes reflected the profound change in her. She was the expression of her very own soul, transparent and radiating love. She remained touched, remembering her feelings and impressions as she journeyed through those places and knew that she needed to return. Her life would never be the same again, regardless of how much she loved them all. They would always be an important part of her life and no matter where she went, they would always be with her.

The contact with her previous world was exactly the same as she had pictured it in one of her visions in Machu Picchu, completely empty. Truthfully, she knew that within Emptiness existed the sum of All, and in that emptiness she had found a space for her New Life. Shazadi every day increased her sensitivity she was free and happy. She had by now concluded all her pending affairs, although in doing so she had to face difficult moments. When finalizing previous life cycles, although it made her happy, she was also aware that it provoked strong reactions in others. However, she had to be firm in her decisions. She had moved much energy within a short period of time and a limited amount of space. The result would be a total transformation. Her family did begin to accept the possibility of her living far away from home, if that is what it took for her to become a fulfilled woman.

New Life,
New Doors.

The Being of Light of Machu Picchu.

PERU

Puma Sinchi was at the airport waiting for her and was very happy that she had decided to change her life and come to live in the Andes. Henceforward, they would start sharing their lives, both at levels of places of spiritual growth as well as with their mutual work they offered to other pilgrims from around the world so that they could take back to other lands the message of power of the Inka Sages.

Shazadi's rebirth in the Andes presented the opportunity to live her life as she had envisioned it in her deep meditations. Little by little they would journey through the other Centers of Power in the Andes and in the rest of the World, with the purpose to anchor and fulfill their personal mission and to expand their wisdom, their inner and outer beauty, their strength and happiness.

Time passed and one day she felt that she and Puma Sinchi ought to consecrate their union in a ceremonial act of marriage. For the occasion they choose the days immediately prior to the September Equinox. The ceremony took place in the Sacred Valley of the Inkas, in a ritual setting among the high mountains and a meditation to commune with Pachamama and Wiraqocha.

Shazadi wished to preserve the moment and shared a poem with her beloved:

PUMA SINCHI

In your eyes there is
a will to grow,
a need to create
that force which makes you live.

Up and down over the mountains you go.
In Machu Picchu you show power.
Like a Puma you stretch out and expand,
quick and strong… 'tis your way of being.

Sensitivity and softness.
The softness of your hands
turn me into a flower.
The willingness to surrender
myself in the Love.

Pyramids and Crystals. Connection with other Centers of Power in the World.

Rebirth from the Deep
Alchemy of the Self.

Manifestation of the Power and its Essence - Tender Sweetness.

EGYPT

Like Children of the Sun, Shazadi and Puma Sinchi were again traveling through the world, and they came to Egypt. Before the plane landed in Cairo, Shazadi began experiencing insights and visions that immersed her in a lot of involvement and complicity with this land. They were taken to Giza, where they would visit some Centers of Power.

The Pyramids represented evidence of one of the greatest cultures to have inhabited our planet. When standing before them there is no other alternative than to honor them and travel in time to remember, through the *Akashic* world, what the Children of the Heavens left for posterity as a sign of their passing.

They had the opportunity to enter the Great Pyramid and ascend to the funerary Chamber of the King. Within that timeless space they followed the ancient Ritual —she lay in the sarcophagus of the King in supine position to embrace the Universe, and he lay prone to embrace the Earth. Thus they reconnected again with all the frequencies in this vital Center of High Vibration. In a few seconds, following respiratory and *mantric* rhythms, they were both transported in time and space to be acknowledged by the Forces of the Earth and the Sky. In this way, they had once again sealed their Solar and Terrestrial history in this land of Egypt.

But the most interesting experience for them took place during one of their meditations in a temple. They succeeded to gain access to the magical world of this land:

Shazadi visualized the richness of their palaces and temples, which were expressions of art and technology wherein the combination of force and sight were expressed at their highest level, always for the benefit of their own inhabitants. She saw herself dancing and celebrating, expressing the subtleness of the body and the art of motion. Then she walked in Egypt remembering when she had dwelled in these lands. She suddenly felt nostalgic, especially so because the heirs of these initiatory monuments were no longer present, but life had to go on.

In another of her visions, an eagle appeared and took her on her wings to other spheres. After soaring with this Bird of Power, she descended and walked along a large passageway in one of the temples where she participated in the meditations carried out by a group of people. All of them held their hands in the prayer position and Shazadi knelt in thankfulness at the opportunity to be there again. She then passed on to another chamber where she began to dance and her movements flowed spontaneously while she listened to soft music connecting her with the energy of Earth and Sky. As her energies expanded she touched everything around her in a gentle manner. She remembered that this had been her ancient art, which she would now have to recover. And in that very instant, Shazadi felt it touch and merge with her and she understood its message of power and sweetness.

It becomes a great challenge when the Self discovers its inner strength and then tries to associate it with tenderness. But was it not one of the philosophies of the Inkas, to be gentle and strong at the same time? Everything is energy and the manner and way we feel, how we perceive ourselves, is totally linked to our Divine Essence. When we enter our heart and breathe with it, we allow our steps to flow in the direction of the deepest purposes of our soul. From that point, and only from that point, do we become fulfilled at all levels and therefore great channels through which creative energy flows. This then is distributed in the form of love and peace all around us.

It is important to know that when we breathe with the mind, we only live on the surface and build on the surface. However, for the real building of our lives, it is necessary to be profound, to travel within our own selves, diving deeply into our inner abyss to discover the real purpose of our Souls.

Contrary to what many people think, we are spiritual beings in need of self-development and not human beings who are in search of spirituality. It is already present within us, but it is necessary to enter into that space. For this, primarily what is needed is confidence, patience and courage. And, when we allow ourselves to enter in this process, we must renounce many things. Then, we can contemplate with the heart the purpose of the soul and go forth with both a firm and delicate step, for it is there that strength is associated with sweetness.

Shazadi, as Universal Pilgrim, was gifted with the opportunity of being in various Centers of Power where she was able to reconnect with parts of her own self that were scattered and in need of returning to their Being. And she perceived that all she had lived, was important to her development, establishing a very strong connection between the Centers of Power, principally those of Egypt and the Andes.

And in that last life, Shazadi had the opportunity of taking up the true PATH OF HER SOUL.

The Sphinx and the Great Pyramid of Egypt.

CONCLUSIONS

I will now analyze Shazadi's processes and courses of action throughout her four lives. As the Great Initiated put it, "What good does a religious life serve, if the legacy of that life, through the actions and deeds of a companion, is a Hell? The greatest achievements in Life are those that leave the most beloved part of you on the road to fulfillment and freedom."

In the course of her life in Egypt, Shazadi was a Princess, with little knowledge of her own self, without experience of her inner strength and still immature, not knowing how to resolve her personal conflicts and insecurities. She surrendered herself to a temporary love, feeling fulfilled by it. This was an example of those moments, in the life of any woman, when she sees herself as a defenseless princess. Her life is empty and she expects love in the form of a prince charming, or a similarly idealized person, to satisfy her incomplete or unredeemed sensations. In any case this will in some way eventually be redeemed, at least partially, and accepted as reality by virtue of family or social pressures.

At the initial stage of a one-to-one relationship of a couple, everything works out marvelously. As Shazadi described it, "Love nourishes, we eat less, sigh constantly, one's skin and complexion transforms, becomes soft and we think of our lover at every instant." This is the reality, for the majority of people, when they enter into a relationship, to seek in each other qualities that they do not possess themselves or at least fail to recognize within them—love and caring—apart from the emotional dependences upon which they place their expectations. As time passes, they accommodate themselves to the relationship and it, in turn, chills, transforming them into virtual strangers. The differences and complaints arise next as a result of what they had conceived within their expectations. There are certainly exceptions, particularly so in the case of more wholesome relationships in which both grow, renewing themselves and maintaining their unity. Both are involved in activities of inner and personal self-improvement, are flexible to changes and agree to share whatever each one gets from the relationship. This is the case of Shazadi and Puma Sinchi, where both seek their own spiritual growth while maintaining mutual respect. It is from this premise that love becomes a daily and self-generating experience, expanding with every passing moment. Mutual consent and support are the principal source of input enabling dialogue to play the part of intermediary contributing to this process of creation.

Poetry expresses sentiments and feelings that evoke romantic part of a relationship. It is an important ingredient of love, a stimulus that motivates dreams, the expression of oneself in verse and song that should never cease to be or disappear.

The individual may indeed grow alone without a partner, it is an option of life. However, it is important to activate one's sexual energy, which is the most powerful in the Universe, insofar as human experience is concerned. For, this energy will assist us to ply the most unfathomable oceans of our reality. We all posses given percentages of the opposite sex and our planet, with its polarities is the master of equilibrium. This is why it is "of the essence" to discover what the Sages of all cultures taught regarding the energy of the Serpent, which in the Eastern tradition is referred to as the force of *Kundalini*. I will be addressing this topic in another work titled, *"Power Women."*

Our passage through this world, at different times and eras, registers in our genetic code the experiences from those lives, whether good and bad. It is up to each person, depending on their level of enlightenment, to gradually cleanse their karmic links with family, culture and society. Aside from this DNA process, the individual is also affected by the setting of the time, which likewise creates habits and customs that are then influenced by education and direct family influence. This last, perhaps, is the most difficult of all to overcome, since it permeates deeply within each individual, all the more so if that individual has not devoted any work to his or her inner self. The nature of this influence is such that few manage to achieve leadership over the members of their family. All of this does not imply that a person should sever these links, quite the opposite. These ties are decided within another dimension, since families are our first teachers and we should honor them, especially so if they follow those rhythms of respect and freedom that one seeks.

At the beginning, Shazadi only looked at her external self. Her spiritual life was conditioned and depended upon feeling pleased and the belief that her freedom was being fulfilled through the mediums of art, poetry, dance, while on a deeper level she seldom felt pleased with herself or others. The search for love, in Egypt, offered her a partial release and happening to be what she was looking for, someone did in fact manage to please her. Hence neither of them actually completed the cycle, since both were "experiencing" life and anything could and, as it turned out, did happen. When a person discovers true "freedom," that person need no longer search outside themselves. Each one of their cells will express that reality, transforming that person into a genuine emissary of love.

In all societies persons move, change jobs, have relationships, marry and/or flee from the home that suckled them in order to feel free. But if they haven't mastered their inner self, this freedom will represent but a mere excuse, for only within ourselves do we find satisfaction. When we are internally free, we are willing to share with someone else our ultimate profound self, without demands or dependences; and that is the path to authenticity. *Love is the most intense experience of freedom and liberation of the self.* A valid reason to follow what a contemporary Sage taught: "Make not love, let love make you." This is the real way.

There will come the moment to discover that it is not necessary to seek in another that which exists within yourself. Then, vain expectations perish and the path of self-awareness will lead us along the eternal way of BEING.

BEING

I AM THE FREEDOM.
I AM THE PEACE.
I AM THE LOVE.
I AM THE JOY.
I AM THE STRENGTH.
I AM THE GENTLENESS.
I AM THE FULFILLMENT OF MY LIFE.
I AM THE LIGHT OF MY BEING.

The litany "Being" will help us in the search and reassertion of our being. The incorporation of this message in our everyday life will strengthen us and, in moments of need, we will find in it an inspirational support to transcend the earthly barriers of our own lives, particularly in our growing phase.

Shazadi had projected on her Egyptian love all that which she herself had not the courage to accept as her own. She accepted love, but accompanied by an emotional demand and, being so, it was incomplete. It was not authentic. It could be termed "love" within the context of dependence, yet in the dimension of the sacred, it was but the whim, typical of the princess who lives in every woman -and the prince that every man wants to be- in this world of structures and dependence. The world is full of such loves and it is precisely there that the delicate part of all this lies, for it is very easy to mix personal appetites with the highest expectations of life. Namely, to be accepted, especially by the being upon whom we believe to be devoting our affection and so-called love. This love is so fleeting that within societies it is sought after everywhere, for at the end of the day people subconsciously seek love outside themselves. That is where they encounter the very first obstacle, since one must first learn to love oneself and only then, with an indispensable amount of wisdom and conscientiousness, realize that we can love and be loved. The risk of societies or individuals where great emotions are not fulfilled from within, is that they foster dependencies and emotional bonds that turn the individual into a slave to their emotions rather than the master of them.

The search for the genuine Self is one of the most difficult quests, since this Self has to be confronted in the process. To breach the barriers of society constitutes a formidable challenge and many individuals, sometimes through family complacency, make of their lives a veritable Drama. By that, I do not mean to imply that one must live alone to avoid confrontations, nor that one should live with someone else in particular throughout their entire life, for these are society's standards. What I am implying is that we should be authentic to our hearts' desire. Bear in mind that everyone's life can be different and it all depends on each person's decision to grow, create and enjoy.

The excuses that one cannot love because we did not receive love from our parents or grandparents or whomever are just that.... mere excuses. The

Universe is far greater than all that and if we have but one day of life, or maybe more, we are already winners and should thank the Universe for granting us a few more hours' worth of opportunities. We should all be instruments of light and love, not of darkness. Let us first realize our power and then love will begin to manifest within us to gradually illuminate our life.

The primary question that a person should ask is, "Do I consider myself happy?" Not just 'happy' in the morning, in the afternoon or at nighttime, but rather, happy in my life or at least most of it! We must be genuine, authentic, without pressures. Let us look at and try to understand our emotions, feelings, needs, disappointments, and shortcomings, strengths and joys. Then, identify what is influencing us, and if various confused thoughts come to mind, seek out the thought or emotion that will transport us to different states of consciousness or harmony, for those will be our guide. If we practice meditation and follow an orderly life and one of gratitude to nature, we will surely find the right way to dispel the conflicts and to start feeling better.

To identify our emotions is important, everything that stems from within us should be our guide and reference point. The fears, angers, sadness, guilt will become a lesson in life if we can perceive the lesson that each holds. We must bear in mind that when we observe these defects, and virtues, is when we transform ourselves into architects of our own feelings. This is one of the great, stepping stones that an individual seeks for growth. To confront our defects and shortcomings while searching for our virtues teaches us that we are much more than we ever imagined, that we are unique beings and the Universe is there to help with us in the pursuit of fulfilling the great dreams of our life. And we should avail ourselves of these opportunities because they may be few and far between.

The excuses that people seek are only an illusion, for after the excuse is over, they must face themselves and if not prepared, what they will see is a monster that will end up devouring them and then blaming them for all their thoughts and actions. The result will be one of dissatisfaction, which will persecute them even in their dreams, that ultimate space where we should all go in search of answers and teachings. Upon each and every one's self discovery, everything changes and then attracts frequencies compatible with Divine Self. These frequencies are the highest in the Universe, because they offer us the possibility of living a magic abundant life.

The axiom that says, "When the Disciple is ready, the Master appears," is not quite so, for the 'Master' is he who realizes when the Disciple has grown and experienced life, the earthly limitations are transcended. When this comes about, the Master will make his appearance to continue his lineage of expanding the wisdom and secrets of life itself. It is thus that, when we are conscious, we attract everything we desire; we are in collaboration with the Universe, which is abundant, unique and infinite, has no competition or match, and is self-sufficient. We thus learn that we were born to be the heirs of this infinite status and that we have the ability to live in richness, joy, health and love.

Every individual possesses a type of hunger, a distinct appetite. Some need professional success and fulfillment, others emotional love, health and so forth. But from the moment in which that person decides to confront their life and ask of themselves if they are on the right path to growth, that person will surely start living more authentically, leaving behind the sense of guilt or victimization. To transcend, that person will have to become charged with solar energy, that will help to cleanse all trappings and emotional burdens, which represents considerable negative baggage of life, for the Universe surely desires something different for each one.

When the individual takes on their own challenges, that person becomes capable of being happy, of transforming everything, and of swimming with the current, and not forces that make everything impossible. This current is the energy of the very Universe that leads to where everything flows in a natural and spontaneous manner.

Shazadi had lived this process during her past life in the Andes, experiencing love and becoming a master in inner alchemy. With her timeless companion she freely shared her knowledge, following the way that all initiates, sooner or later, have to experience. In that respect her birth in Egypt was a subliminal era, where she counted as an ally her own discipline through dance and meditation. She wished to live the experience of being a princess, who could have anything she wanted and the result of that phase of her apprenticeship was the acknowledgement that in the spiritual world nothing can be bought, only conquered through sweetness and freedom. Love spawns

The process of successive stages of liberation of Shazadi in Egypt was based on detaching and renouncing power in order to attain the essence of simplicity and genuineness, hence that life confronted her with herself. In the Andes, the experience almost repeated itself, but the beauty of Pachamama and the light of Wiraqocha indicated to her that freedom is essentially beauty itself, and it possesses no form or color.

Her lives, in so many Sacred Lands, had served the purpose of confirming to her that when the being is so disposed, the richness of the Universe is manifested in life at its highest levels. Sages of all ages had happily toiled in Egypt, Rapa Nui, the Andes and Mexico in search of integrating with the Divine, the Eternal. And these lives served the purpose for Shazadi to be connected to her divine self—the invocation to the Sacredness in each being throughout all ages that her soul would always continue. This will enable her subsequent births to no longer bear blame but in its stead only gratification at fulfilling her own mission of being happy and spreading this message among her own world.

Shazadi, in her latest life in the land of the Mayas and Aztecs understood that everything was interconnected so she was able to unravel answers, close cycles, discover episodes of the past and finally achieve freedom. For their part, the Andes showed her the essence of beauty and power. They taught her that one dies and is reborn every day and that some deaths are forever since they prepare the self for a new birth and for that reason one must be free of energetic and emotional burdens.

Puma Sinchi had likewise undergone several rebirths and was now free in many aspects and it would be Shazadi who would complement him in the other acts of life. In this way both of them would be one of the couples that would reflect the encounter of twin souls and would be recognized in time and space in gratification by this generation. Since this was the reflection of alchemy in both the physical and energetic temples therefore surely expand this wisdom in the inheritance of the sons and daughters of the Sun and the Earth.

Shazadi's Cosmic Stone represented the beliefs that a person may hold, most importantly by intention, to accept that the best is reserved for them. She learned that it was possible to transmute the sufferings, pains, and guilt, and it is important to have a daily discipline in search of inner secrets to feel better. Meditation is the most precious ally for harmony and serenity, the door we open to peace and beauty, which leads to a better quality of life of the body, the mind and the soul.

Upon waking and greeting the Sun every morning, thanking it for this new opportunity, we must always ask permission since we enter upon spaces of gratitude and liberty that represent the Sun. The Sunsets should be moments of reflection and thankfulness for what has been lived during the course of the day, where the soul is allowed to express and enlighten our life, preparing it for the new dawn. Gratitude must be present from the moment in which the Sun appears until the moment it sets.

Let us allow Pachamama and the Spirit of Wiraqocha to bless our lives, let us open our hearts and expand their light to the hearts of those who think that love is not part of their lives. Let us ask for the protection and guidance of the Guardians of the Universe, who are our own guides, for the light to illuminate our world and peace to be manifest in all the creatures of the Earth. Let us always wish for and invoke that freedom radiates our Pachamama, for the Universal Mother to protect us, shelter us, and with affection show us the beauties of the life. Let us feel that her heart beats to the rhythm of the heart of the world and the Universe.

Life turns into more life.
We are the pulsation of the energies.
We are the Universal Love.

Thankful for existing, thankful for Life.
Thankful for the nourishment that we receive.
Thankful for loving us as your children.
Thankful for your protection.
Thankful for every moment.

Good journey of Light.
And remember to care for your heart.
In the silence, we leave behind the words.
That we no longer need.
In silence we can speak with a gaze.
In silence we speak with the eyes of the heart.

With Love, Shazadi

The book *"The Pilgrim"*
was printed in Danny's Graff
Calle Quera No. 238 Telefax: 084-240932
Cusco - Perú